Raintree Steck-Vaughn

Illustrated
SCIENCE
ENCYCLOPEDIA

Volume
9

FUN – GYR

RSVP
**RAINTREE
STECK-VAUGHN**
P U B L I S H E R S
The Steck-Vaughn Company

Austin, Texas

Published by Raintree Steck-Vaughn Publishers, an imprint of
Steck-Vaughn Company.

Executive Editor	Diane Sharpe
Senior Editor	Anne Souby
Design Manager	Joyce Spicer

This edition edited and designed by Andromeda Oxford Ltd.

Andromeda Editorial and Design

Project Manager	Julia Roles
Editorial Manager	Jenny Fry
Design	TT Designs, T&S Truscott
Cover Design	John Barker

Library of Congress Cataloging-in-Publication Data
Raintree Steck-Vaughn illustrated science encyclopedia.
        p.   cm.
    Includes bibliographical references and index.
    Summary: A twenty-four volume set containing brief articles
on science topics.
    ISBN 0-8172-3943-X (set)
    ISBN 0-8172-3927-8 (Volume 9)
    1. Science—Encyclopedias, Juvenile.   [1. Science—
Encyclopedias.]   I. Raintree Steck-Vaughn Publishers.
Q121.R354   1997
503—dc20   96-11078
                                   CIP
                                   AC

Printed and Bound in the United States of America.
1 2 3 4 5 6 7 8 9 10 IP 00 99 98 97 96

USING THE RAINTREE STECK-VAUGHN ILLUSTRATED SCIENCE ENCYCLOPEDIA

You are living in a world in which science, technology, and nature are very important. You see something about science almost every day. It might be on television, in the newspaper, in a book at school, or some other place. Often, you want more information about what you see.

The *Raintree Steck-Vaughn Illustrated Science Encyclopedia* will help you find what you want to know. It contains information on many science subjects. You may want to find out about computers, the environment, space exploration, biology, agriculture, or mathematics, for example. They are all in the *Raintree Steck-Vaughn Illustrated Science Encyclopedia.* There are many, many other subjects covered as well.

There are twenty-four volumes in the encyclopedia. The articles, which are called entries, are in alphabetical order through the first twenty-two volumes. On the spine of each volume, below the volume number, are some letters. The letters above the line are the first three letters of the first entry in that volume. The letters below the line are the first three letters of the last entry in that volume. In Volume 1, for example, you see that the first entry begins with **AAR** and that the last entry begins with **ANT**. Using the letters makes it easy to find the volume you need.

In Volume 23, there are three special features—reference charts and tables, a bibliography, and an index. In Volume 24, there are interesting projects that you can do on your own. The projects are fun to do, and they help you discover and understand important science principles. Many can give you ideas that can help you develop your own science fair projects.

Main Entries There are two kinds of main entries in the *Raintree Steck-Vaughn Illustrated Science Encyclopedia.* Many of the entries are major topics that are spread over several pages. The titles of these entries are shown at the top of the page in a yellow box. Other entries required less space to cover the topic fully. The titles of these main entries are printed in capital letters. They look like this: **ABALONE**. At the beginning of some entries, you will see a phonetic pronunciation of the entry title, such as (ăb′ ə lō′ nē).

In the front of each volume, there is a pronunciation key. Use it the same way you use your dictionary's pronunciation key.

Cross-References Within the main entries are cross-references referring to other entries in the encyclopedia. Within an entry, they look like this: (see MAMMAL). At the end of an entry, they look like this: *See also* HYENA. These cross-references tell you where to find other helpful information on the subject you are reading about.

Projects At the end of some entries, you will see this symbol: 🖎 PROJECT 1. It tells you which projects related to that entry are in Volume 24.

Illustrations There are thousands of photographs, drawings, graphs, diagrams, tables, and other illustrations in the *Raintree Steck-Vaughn Illustrated Science Encyclopedia.* They will help you better understand the entries you read. Captions describe the illustrations. Many of the illustrations also have labels that point out important parts.

Activities Some main entries include activities presented in a special box. These activities are short projects that give you a chance to work with science on your own.

Index In Volume 23, the index lists every main entry by volume and page number. Many subjects that are not main entries are also listed in the index, as well as the illustrations, projects, activities, and reference charts and tables.

Bibliography In Volume 23, there is also a bibliography for students. The books in this list are on a variety of topics and can supplement what you have learned in the *Raintree Steck-Vaughn Illustrated Science Encyclopedia.*

The *Raintree Steck-Vaughn Illustrated Science Encyclopedia* was designed especially for you, the student. It is a source of knowledge for the world of science, technology, and nature. Enjoy it!

PRONUNCIATION KEY

Each symbol has the same sound as the darker letters in the sample words.

ə	balloon, ago	îr	deer, pier	r	root, tire
ă	map, have	j	join, germ	s	so, press
ā	day, made	k	king, ask	sh	shoot, machine
âr	care, bear	l	let, cool	t	to, stand
ä	father, car	m	man, same	th	thin, death
b	ball, rib	n	no, turn	*th*	then, this
ch	choose, nature	ng	bring, long	ŭ	up, cut
d	did, add	ŏ	odd, pot	ûr	urge, hurt
ě	bell, get	ō	cone, know	v	view, give
ē	sweet, easy	ô	all, saw	w	wood, glowing
f	fan, soft	oi	boy, boil	y	yes, year
g	good, big	ou	now, loud	z	zero, raise
h	hurt, ahead	o͝o	good, took	zh	leisure, vision
ĭ	rip, ill	o͞o	boot, noon	'	strong accent
ī	side, sky	p	part, scrap	´	weak accent

GUIDE TO MEASUREMENT ABBREVIATIONS

All measurements in the *Raintree Steck-Vaughn Illustrated Science Encyclopedia* are given in both the customary system and the metric system [in brackets like these]. Following are the abbreviations used for various units of measure.

Customary Units of Measure

mi. = miles	cu. yd. = cubic yards
m.p.h. = miles per hour	cu. ft. = cubic feet
yd. = yards	cu. in. = cubic inches
ft. = feet	gal. = gallons
in. = inches	pt. = pints
sq. mi. = square miles	qt. = quarts
sq. yd. = square yards	lb. = pounds
sq. ft. = square feet	oz. = ounces
sq. in. = square inches	fl. oz. = fluid ounces
cu. mi. = cubic miles	°F = degrees Fahrenheit

Metric Units of Measure

km = kilometers	cu. km = cubic kilometers
kph = kilometers per hour	cu. m = cubic meters
m = meters	cu. cm = cubic centimeters
cm = centimeters	ml = milliliters
mm = millimeters	kg = kilograms
sq. km = square kilometers	g = grams
sq. m = square meters	mg = milligrams
sq. cm = square centimeters	°C = degrees Celsius

For information on how to convert customary measurements to metric measurements, see the Metric Conversions table in Volume 23.

The fungi (plural of *fungus*) are a large group of organisms that have some characteristics similar to certain algae and protozoans (see ALGAE; PROTOZOA). Fungi are not, however, related to either of these two groups. Fungi were once classified as simple, nongreen plants, belonging to a subkingdom of the plant kingdom. Now, most scientists classify fungi in their own kingdom (see CLASSIFICATION OF LIVING ORGANISMS). More than 100,000 species of fungi are known.

Fungi are extremely versatile organisms. They live throughout the world in every imaginable environment. Some familiar fungi are mildew, molds, mushrooms, rusts, smuts, and yeasts. Slime molds are often considered fungi, though there is some disagreement about this classification (see SLIME MOLD).

Structure of the fungus Some of the one-celled fungi, such as yeasts, are little more than spore cases (see SPORE). Most fungi, however, have a body made up of chains of cells, or filaments, called hyphae. A large mass of hyphae is called a mycelium. A mycelium usually smothers or invades a source of food and secretes digestive juices over it. The dissolved food is then absorbed by the fungus. Some fungi attack living plants and animals, but most of them feed on dead matter, often in the soil. Often, a large fruiting body grows from the mycelium. The fruiting body contains many spores that, when released, will grow into new fungi. In the mushroom, the mycelium is underground,

POISONOUS FUNGUS

The fly agaric, or amanita, is very poisonous. Eating it causes vomiting and even death.

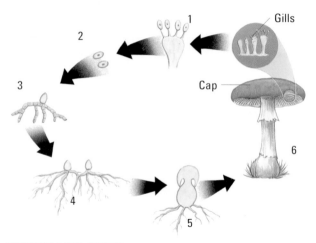

FUNGUS LIFE CYCLE

Fungi have a complex life cycle. (1 and 2) Spores form on a mushroom's gills. (3) The spores germinate, producing threads. (4) The threads fuse together. (5) Fruiting bodies form on the tangle of threads. (6) The fruiting body grows into a mature mushroom, with gills.

where it absorbs food from decaying matter in the soil. The fruiting body is the umbrella-shaped structure that grows above the ground. It is this fruiting body that is often considered the "mushroom." Fungi range in size from a microscopic yeast cell at 0.000004 in. [0.0001 mm] to a giant species of mushroom measuring more than 38 in. [96 cm] across.

Life of the fungus Because fungi contain no chlorophyll, they cannot produce their own food (see PHOTOSYNTHESIS). They must get food from some other source. In order for a fungus to "eat," it secretes enzymes into its food. These enzymes start the digestion of complex foods into simple compounds (see COMPOUND; ENZYME). The fungus then absorbs these digested foods into its hyphae.

Different species of fungi get their food from different sources and in different ways. Parasitic fungi feed on living plants and animals (see PARASITE). Parasitic fungi cause many diseases in their hosts and usually have to be controlled with fungicides. A fungicide is a chemical used to kill harmful types of fungi (see FUNGICIDE). Saprophytic fungi feed on dead and decaying plant and animal matter. They are vital parts of the food chain (see FOOD CHAIN; SAPROPHYTE). Symbiotic fungi share a mutually helpful relationship with some other organisms (see SYMBIOSIS). Lichens consist of algae

and fungi living in partnership. A mycorrhiza is a partnership between a fungus and the roots of a plant, such as an orchid or a forest tree. The roots give the fungus shelter, food, and water. The fungus, on the other hand, supplies nitrogen, zinc, phosphorus, and other minerals to the plant.

Most fungi can reproduce asexually by producing spores that grow into new fungi. Some fungi, such as yeast, reproduce asexually by budding. Others split by fission. Most fungi also have a sexual reproduction stage during their life cycles, producing spores that act like gametes. They combine to form a zygote, which develops into a new fungus (see ASEXUAL REPRODUCTION; REPRODUCTION).

Importance of fungi Fungi can be harmful or helpful to human beings and other organisms. Parasitic fungi cause many harmful plant diseases, such as blight, mildew, rust, and smut. Blight destroyed the potato crop in Ireland in the 1840s. This caused a famine in which about 750,000 people starved to death. In addition to the damage it causes to plants, mildew can destroy clothing and

ACTIVITY   *Mushroom spores*

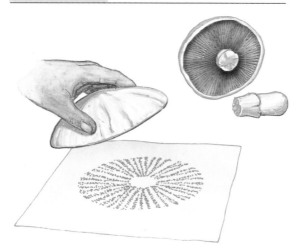

Cut the stalk from a ripe mushroom and lay the cap on a sheet of paper. Use white paper if your mushroom has dark gills, and colored paper if it has white gills. Cover the cap with a bowl. Leave it for a few hours and then carefully lift the bowl and the cap. You will see that hundreds of thousands of spores have fallen from the gills and produced a gill-like pattern on the paper. **Caution: Do not eat the mushrooms or the spores.**

books stored in damp places. Mold ruins millions of dollars' worth of food every year.

One type of plant fungus, ergot, grows on rye and other grains. It can be processed to produce several powerful drugs, including LSD. LSD (lysergic acid diethylamide) is a hallucinogen (see HALLUCINO-GEN). Ergotism, or St. Anthony's fire, is a disease that affects people and animals that eat grains infected with ergot fungus. This disease is incurable and causes convulsions and death. Some diseases, such as ringworm, are caused by a fungus that invades the skin and is easily passed from one person to another. Many varieties of mushrooms are poisonous and can cause sickness and even death if eaten.

There are many helpful types of fungi, however. Saprophytic fungi (along with bacteria) are an important part of the food chain. In the process of getting food for themselves, the fungi help decompose dead plant and animal matter (see DECOMPOSITION). They break down food into simple molecules, releasing many minerals and other chemicals needed by plants.

FUNGUS SHAPES
The puffballs (left) contain many thousands of seedlike spores. The elf-cup fungus (right) is also known as orange-peel fungus because of its color and shape. The parasitic fungus *Tremella* (below) grows on the bark of dead trees.

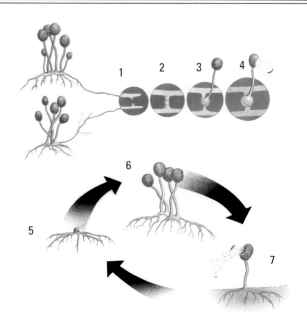

MOLD LIFE CYCLE

In sexual reproduction (1) hyphae (threads) from molds of different "sexes" grow together. (2) When they touch, they join together. (3) The joint swells and produces a sporangium (spore case). (4) The sporangium bursts, releasing the spores. In asexual reproduction of a mold, (5) spores germinate to form a mycelium. (6) Sporangia then form on the mycelium. (7) The sporangia burst, releasing more spores.

Some fungi are used as foods. Mushrooms are a popular food in most parts of the world. They grow rapidly and are easily cultivated. Certain molds are added to cheeses, such as camembert and roquefort, to provide a sharp flavor and to help ripen the cheese.

Yeasts are eaten as a source of protein and B vitamins. Yeasts are also used in fermentation of certain grains (see FERMENTATION). In fermentation, yeast changes sugar into carbon dioxide gas and alcohol. The carbon dioxide provides the carbonation (bubbling) in many beverages. Yeast is also used in making bread products, releasing carbon dioxide and causing the dough to rise (see BREAD).

Some molds are used to produce antibiotics and other drugs. The most famous of these, penicillin, was first processed from a mold in 1929.

See also ANTIBIOTIC; PENICILLIN.

EDIBLE FUNGUS

The honey fungus (below) gets its name from its sweet-tasting flavor.

FURNACE A furnace is any enclosed structure in which fuel is burned to produce heat. A furnace is usually made of metal or brick, or a combination of these or other fireproof substances. Furnaces are designed to produce the greatest amount of heat from the fuel used. They are also designed to direct the heat where it is most needed. Furnaces are used to produce heat for comfort. They are also used to boil water to make steam or to heat various substances.

There are two main groups of furnaces. The first group consists of furnaces used for heating homes and other buildings (see CENTRAL HEATING). Home furnaces must be cared for regularly. Cleaning furnaces maintains their efficiency. It also helps prevent fires. All furnaces, chimneys, and air ducts should be serviced once a year.

The second group of furnaces are used in industry. They are used mainly to heat metals and to make steam for various purposes. They are also used in making bricks, cement, glass, steel, and many other materials. Industrial furnaces produce extremely high temperatures. Many of them use coal or coke for fuel. One industrial furnace, the blast furnace, is a cone-shaped structure of brick, concrete, or steel. The blast furnace is used to fuse, or melt, iron ore with coke to make pig iron. Fans blow air under pressure into the furnace. This makes the fire extremely hot (see BLAST FURNACE).

Electric furnaces are widely used in industry.

Metalworkers often need temperatures ranging from 3,500°F to 5,000°F [1,830°C to 2,800°C] to heat metal for shaping. Electric furnaces can produce these temperatures. There are three main types of electric furnaces. In arc furnaces, heat comes from an electric arc formed between carbon electrodes (see ELECTRODE). A resistance furnace works like a bread toaster. A resistance furnace produces heat by passing an electric current through heating coils. The coils, in resisting the electric current, become very hot. An induction furnace sends an alternating current through a conductor (see ALTERNATING CURRENT; INDUCTION). The conductor is wrapped around an insulated container. The container holds the material that is to be heated or melted. The alternating current produces a changing magnetic field (see ELECTROMAGNETISM). This changing magnetic field causes an electric current to flow in the material. The induced current heats the material. If a material, such as glass, does not allow induced currents to be set up with it, the container is usually made of carbon. In these cases, the induction furnace produces heat within the container. In turn, the container melts the material.

Atomic furnaces, also called nuclear reactors, are designed to produce power by nuclear fission. Their fuel is usually uranium or plutonium (see NUCLEAR ENERGY).

Solar furnaces produce temperatures of 8,000°F [4,400°C] or higher. In a solar furnace, a group

FURNACE
Industrial furnaces produce very high temperatures. Industrial furnaces are used to make steam, heat metals, and make such products as bricks and glass.

of mirrors focuses the sun's rays to a specific spot in an oven.

See also KILN; SOLAR ENERGY.

PROJECT 51

FUSE, ELECTRIC An electric fuse is a device that breaks an electric circuit when the current becomes too large. The current may become too large because of a short circuit or an overload of electricity. A short circuit occurs when two wires supplying electricity accidentally touch one another. A large surge of current then flows through the wires. This can cause the wires to overheat and start a fire. An overload occurs when too many appliances are plugged into a single power supply circuit. Again, the wires of the circuit are carrying more current than they can safely handle. The fuse prevents these occurrences from happening (see CIRCUIT, ELECTRIC; CURRENT, ELECTRIC).

The fuse usually consists of a thin metal strip or wire that is attached to two terminals inside a cylindrical housing. The housing either screws or plugs into an electric circuit between the main power line and the house wiring. Electric current flows into the house circuit only when the fuse is in place and is in working order. When a large surge of current flows through the metal strip in the fuse, it quickly melts. The strip is made from a special alloy that melts at low temperature (see ALLOY). A gap is created in the strip. This prevents electric current from flowing into the house circuit where it could cause trouble. Thus, an electric fuse is a kind of circuit breaker (see CIRCUIT BREAKER).

There are two kinds of house fuses: plug fuses and cartridge fuses. Both types have small windows so that it is possible to see if the metal strip is still in one piece. Plug fuses screw into sockets and carry light electrical loads. They are used in circuits that supply current for lights and small appliances. Cartridge fuses are long, narrow cylinders that slide into brackets. They carry heavier electrical loads for items such as electric stoves and clothes washers. Fuses are found mainly in older houses. Most modern houses are required to have circuit breakers.

Fuses are made in a variety of current ratings according to the maximum current they can carry. Most house fuses are rated between 15 and 25 amperes (see AMPERE). If a low-rated fuse is placed in a higher-rated circuit, it burns out immediately. A high-rated fuse in a lower-rated circuit is dangerous. It allows too much current to flow into the circuit. The excess current can burn out small appliances and cause wires to overheat. Sometimes, people try to replace a burned-out plug fuse with a copper penny. The penny closes the circuit and allows current to flow. However, the penny does nothing to prevent a short circuit or overload.

FUSION The term *fusion* generally refers to the change that takes place when a solid turns into a liquid. The melting of ice is fusion. The melting of any metal when it is heated is also fusion.

Heat is required to produce fusion. The heat energy absorbed during fusion helps separate the molecules of a substance (see MOLECULE). The now-molten (melted) substance contains more energy than when it was a solid. For example, a pound of water contains more energy than a pound of ice.

The heat required to produce fusion does not change the temperature of the substance while it is actually melting. The heat goes toward increasing the distance between the molecules, so that they move more freely. The heat that is gained during fusion is called the latent heat of fusion (see LATENT HEAT).

FUSION—Tokamak reactor
The fusion test reactor at Princeton University is the type called a Tokamak. It is a donut-shaped vessel surrounded by coils of wire. An electric current flowing through the coils creates a strong magnetic field. The field concentrates the hot fusion gases in the center of the "donut."

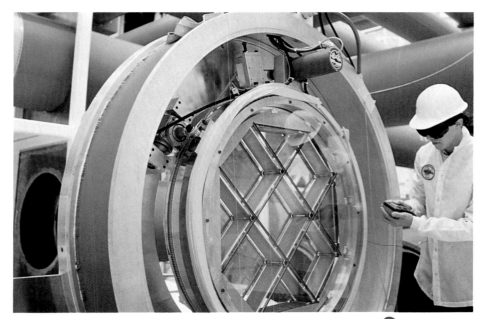

FUSION—Lasers
Scientists are experimenting with powerful lasers, such as here at the Livermore Laboratory in California, to produce controlled nuclear fusion reactions.

FUSION—Nuclear
Nuclear fusion occurs when two light atomic nuclei join together to form a heavier nucleus, releasing energy in the process. Below left, two deuterium nuclei, each with one proton and one neutron, collide to form a helium nucleus and a neutron, releasing a great deal of energy. Below right, a deuterium nucleus collides with a lithium nucleus. The nuclei fuse to form a beryllium nucleus and a neutron, releasing more energy.

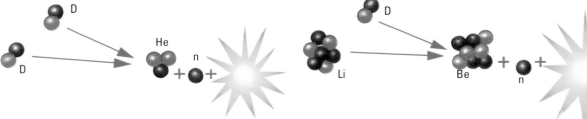

Nuclear fusion The term *fusion* is also used by nuclear physicists (see NUCLEAR PHYSICS). When they use the term, it means "joining together." Specifically, nuclear fusion means the joining together of two or more atomic nuclei (plural of *nucleus*), such as those of deuterium. Deuterium is an isotope of hydrogen (see HYDROGEN; ISOTOPE; NUCLEUS). Two deuterium nuclei naturally repel each other. To overcome this, the nuclei are sent toward each other at very high speeds. One of the ways these high speeds can be reached is to heat the nuclei to over 1,800,032°F [1,000,000°C]. When the two nuclei hit each other and fuse, they form the nucleus of a helium atom and an extra neutron. The new nucleus weighs less than the two original nuclei. This missing mass has been converted to energy.

Albert Einstein was the first to explain that mass and energy are different aspects of the same thing, in his theory of relativity (see EINSTEIN, ALBERT; RELATIVITY). The energy produced by fusion is referred to as thermonuclear energy. The energy of the sun is thermonuclear energy. The energy of the hydrogen bomb is also produced by nuclear fusion (see NUCLEAR WEAPONS; SUN).

The high temperatures required for fusion to occur are very difficult to produce and control. Because of this, scientists have not yet found a way to make fusion a practical source of energy. Scientists are working to overcome these problems. Thus, reactors in nuclear power plants still use another type of nuclear reaction called fission to produce energy. Fission involves splitting a nucleus (see FISSION; NUCLEAR ENERGY).

Cold fusion In 1989, an English scientist and an American scientist said they had discovered "cold fusion." They said they had done an experiment in which they had produced fusion without using high temperatures. The possibility of cold fusion was exciting because it meant that fusion could now be a practical source of energy. However, other scientists were not able to reproduce the results of the cold fusion experiment. After careful review, many scientists now discount the experiment. *See also* COLD FUSION; ENERGY.

G

GAGARIN, YURI ALEKSEYEVICH

(1934–1968) Yuri Gagarin was the first person to orbit the earth in a spacecraft. He was a major in the former Soviet Air Force. On April 12, 1961, he was launched in the spacecraft *Vostok 1*. The flight went as far as 203 mi. [327 km] above the surface of the earth. It made one orbit, which took 1 hour and 48 minutes. The spacecraft was 125 ft. [38 m] long when it left the launch pad. Most of it was burned up in space. Gagarin returned to earth in a spherical capsule just 7.5 ft. [228 cm] wide.

Soon after Gagarin's flight, two American astronauts were launched into space. A year later, John Glenn was the first American to go into orbit (see GLENN, JOHN HERSCHEL). Seven years after Gagarin's space flight, he was killed in an airplane crash.

GALÁPAGOS ISLANDS

The Galápagos Islands are a group of fifteen small volcanic islands near the equator in the Pacific Ocean. They are approximately 600 mi. [960 km] from the coast of Ecuador, to which they belong. The main islands are Isabela, San Cristóbal, San Salvador, Santa Cruz, and Santa Maria. There are some active volcanoes, up to 5,000 ft. [1,524 m] high. Cactus, mesquite, and thorn trees grow inland, with mangroves near the shores. The islands are home to some giant tortoises and many other unusual reptiles, including the marine iguana, which is the world's only marine lizard.

The Galápagos Islands are best known for providing Charles Darwin with much of the information upon which he based his theory of evolution (see DARWIN, CHARLES; EVOLUTION). A group of thirteen finches, now known as Darwin's finches, were very important to Darwin's ideas. Although the birds differ in size and plumage, and also in their feeding habits and their beaks, they are all basically alike. Darwin concluded that a long time ago one kind of finch had managed to get to the islands from the mainland and had gradually evolved into the present-day species. Because there were so few other small birds on the islands, the finches were able to branch out and make use of many different foods. In other words, they filled the roles or ecological niches occupied by different kinds of birds in other parts of the world. Some specialized in eating insects and their beaks became quite slender, while others specialized in eating seeds and developed much heavier beaks. The birds on different islands also evolved in slightly different ways. The one original finch species eventually produced the thirteen species that live on the Galápagos Islands today.

GALÁPAGOS ISLANDS

The aptly named Pinnacle Rock sticks up on the shore of a bay at Bartolomé Island in the Galápagos Islands.

A galaxy (gǎl'ǝk sē) is a large group of stars held together by gravity (see GRAVITY; STAR). Galaxies may also contain gases and large clouds of dust. Most of the stars in a typical galaxy surround a dense cluster of stars that form the nucleus, or core, of the galaxy. Gravitational attraction of the nucleus keeps the stars of a galaxy from flying off into space. The rotational motion of the galaxy keeps the stars from collapsing into the nucleus.

The total number of galaxies in the universe is unknown. Millions of galaxies have been seen with telescopes, but there may be trillions. The smallest of the known galaxies contains about a billion stars. Most galaxies contain billions of stars. The same gravitational forces that keep the parts of one galaxy together also act to form groups of galaxies.

It has been found that all distant galaxies are moving apart from each other. Furthermore, the more distant galaxies are moving apart at higher speeds than closer galaxies. This is evidence for the expansion of the universe.

Shapes and sizes There are two main kinds of galaxies—spiral and elliptical.

Spiral galaxies are disk-shaped, with a bulging nucleus at the center. Surrounding the disk is a halo of faint, older stars. The halos also contain extremely hot interstellar gases. (*Interstellar* means "among the stars.") Two or more arms extend in a spiral pattern from the center of the galaxy. Clouds of dust and gases exist throughout a spiral galaxy. The Milky Way is a spiral galaxy (see MILKY WAY).

Elliptical galaxies are shaped like a globe. Some are round, and some are flattened. Elliptical galaxies have less dust and gases than spiral galaxies. Elliptical galaxies also rotate more slowly. A few

ANDROMEDA GALAXY

Andromeda is an elliptical galaxy located about 2.2 million light-years (13 trillion miles) away from the earth. This photograph was taken using the 200-inch telescope at Mount Palomar in southern California.

galaxies are neither spiral nor elliptical. They are irregular in shape and seem to consist only of young stars.

Because galaxies are so great in size, they are measured in light-years. A light-year is the distance light travels in one year. Light travels at 186,282

GALAXY SHAPES

The three main types of galaxies are named for their shapes: spiral (left), elliptical (center), and irregular (right).

mi. [299,792 km] per second. Therefore, one light-year equals 5.88 trillion mi. [9.46 trillion km]. The diameter of a typical spiral galaxy is about 100,000 light-years. That means it takes light 100,000 years to travel from one end of the galaxy to the other.

Except for irregular galaxies, a galaxy rotates around an imaginary axis passing through its nucleus. It takes a spiral galaxy about 200 million years to complete one rotation.

Evolution of galaxies The seeds of the modern galaxies were sown soon after the big bang, some 15 billion years ago. As the universe expanded from the big bang, hot clouds of hydrogen and helium were formed (see BIG BANG THEORY). In some regions there were slightly more dense concentrations of gas. According to the most widely accepted theory of galaxy formation, clusters of stars formed from these pockets of denser gas. The star clusters floated through space, meeting and combining with other clusters. This process continued until large clusters of stars, called protogalaxies, were formed. Once a protogalaxy had formed, gravity pulled the stars toward the center of each cluster. The largest stars settled around the center of the group to form a galactic nucleus.

The gravitational pull of nearby protogalaxies causes an evolving protogalaxy to spin slightly. If the spin is small, the galaxy will adopt a spherical or elliptical shape. Faster-spinning protogalaxies form a disk of gas around the galactic nucleus. Gas in the disk forms into stars and a spiral galaxy results. Just why the stars form into arms in spiral galaxies is still unknown.

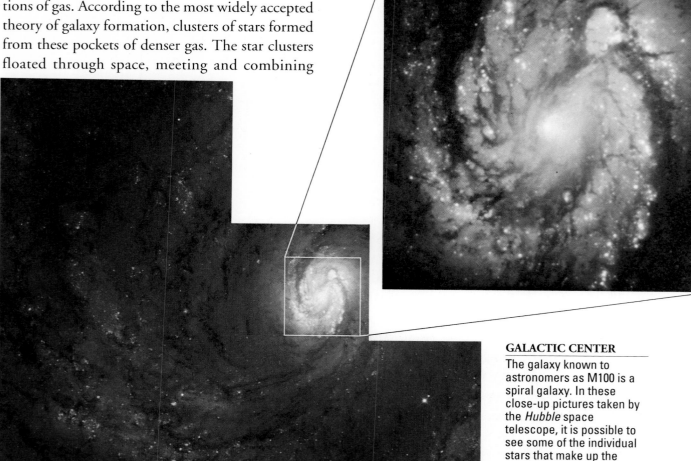

GALACTIC CENTER
The galaxy known to astronomers as M100 is a spiral galaxy. In these close-up pictures taken by the *Hubble* space telescope, it is possible to see some of the individual stars that make up the galaxy's central nucleus.

The Milky Way Our sun is one of the stars that make up the galaxy called the Milky Way. The Milky Way is a spiral galaxy that has about 100 billion stars and is about 100,000 light-years in diameter.

Observation of the Milky Way by astronomers has found it to have a distinct, bright core. The core contains a small, very bright body that radiates strong radio waves but whose nature is unknown. The number of stars within two light-years of the center of the Milky Way is thought to be several million.

The spiral disk that makes up the Milky Way is approximately 1,000 light-years thick. Our sun is located inside the disk and is one of the stars that makes up a spiral arm of the galaxy.

Astronomers can see the Milky Way galaxy only as a rather narrow band of stars. Most stars in the galaxy, including those of the nucleus, are hidden from view by gigantic clouds of dust. The immense number of stars that make up the plane of the disk can sometimes be seen as a faintly glowing band that arches across the night sky from one horizon to the other.

Recent study of the Milky Way by astronomers and chemists indicates that the galaxy is a giant ring of star-bearing clouds, with the sun located on the outer edge of the ring. Within the ring, new stars are always being formed. At the same time, dying stars in the nucleus are supplying new dust clouds to the ring. The sun travels in orbit around the nucleus at a speed of about 558,000 m.p.h. [897,800 kph]. It completes one orbit in 260 million years.

The Milky Way is one galaxy in a group of galaxies. Of these, the Andromeda galaxy is nearest to the Milky Way. The Andromeda galaxy is faintly visible to the eye in the Andromeda constellation (see CONSTELLATION). It is two million light-years from the Milky Way. It is one-third larger in diameter and has twice as many stars as the Milky Way. Like some other galaxies, Andromeda has two small satellite galaxies orbiting it. The Milky Way has three (only two visible) small, irregular satellite galaxies, called the Magellanic Clouds. *See also* ASTRONOMY; SOLAR SYSTEM; UNIVERSE.

SPIRAL GALAXY

When seen from above or below, a spiral galaxy reveals its rotating arms of stars (top). But viewed from the side (bottom), the arms disappear but the center (nucleus) of the galaxy still shines brightly.

GALEN (A.D. 129–199) Galen was a Greek doctor. He was born at Pergamum in Asia Minor. The Roman Empire was vast in Galen's lifetime, and he studied in Greece, Egypt, and Rome. He was surgeon to the gladiators at Pergamum in A.D. 157. In 162, he went to Rome, where he was the personal physician of five emperors before he died.

Galen made many discoveries about medicine and anatomy, such as that injury on the right side of the brain causes disorder on the left side of the body. He wrote hundreds of books, which were used by Arab and European doctors for centuries.

GALENA (gə lē′nə) Galena is the main ore from which lead is extracted (see LEAD; ORE). Galena is a soft, heavy, metallic gray mineral. It is a lead sulfide. Sulfides are minerals that contain sulfur in combination with metals. By weight, galena is 87 percent lead and 13 percent sulfur. Galena is known for its perfect cubic cleavage. This means that, when struck, it breaks into cubes along definite breakage lines called cleavage planes. It is commonly found in masses in limestone or as fragments in sediment. Some deposits of galena contain silver and are refined to obtain both lead and silver. The chemical formula for galena is PbS. The chief sources of galena are Canada, Australia, Germany, Mexico, the former Soviet Union, and the United States.

See also MINERAL.

GALILEO (1564–1642) Galileo is the name commonly used for Galileo Galilei, an Italian physicist. He was one of the first scientists to use modern scientific methods. He lived in an age when the Roman Catholic church was very powerful. Science was generally considered a threat to the ideas of Christianity. Galileo's work brought him into conflict with Christian beliefs of the time.

Galileo studied at the University of Pisa. While he was in the cathedral there, he made his first discovery. He saw that the hanging lights swung steadily from side to side in the draft. He did experiments to show that this movement was regular enough to measure time. This discovery was used sixty years later in making clocks with pendulums.

GALILEO

Galileo was a mathematician and a physicist. His invention of the telescope also made him an astronomer.

Galileo became professor of mathematics at Pisa. He is supposed to have proved his ideas about gravity by dropping different weights from the top of the Leaning Tower of Pisa. His beliefs were against the ideas of the ancient Greek philosopher Aristotle. Because of this, Galileo was forced to leave the university.

Galileo went to the city of Padua in northeastern Italy in 1592 and began work on a telescope. With his telescope, he discovered mountains and craters on the moon and saw for the first time the four largest moons of Jupiter. His discoveries led him to believe that the earth and planets move around the sun, as Copernicus had said. The Roman Catholic church, however, believed that the sun moved around the earth. Galileo was accused of heresy (going against church teachings) in 1633. He would not deny what he had seen through his telescope. Galileo was found guilty and was imprisoned in a house in Florence for the rest of his life. In 1984, the Roman Catholic church formally acknowledged that it was wrong in condemning Galileo.

See also ARISTOTLE; COPERNICUS.

GALLBLADDER The gallbladder is a small baglike organ found in most animals with a backbone, including humans. The gallbladder lies close to the liver. It stores and concentrates a greenish yellow fluid called bile. Bile is produced by the liver and flows into the gallbladder. Bile contains special chemicals, called bile acids, that help break down fatty foods in the small intestine (see DIGESTION). Food passing into the small intestine causes the release of a hormone called cholecystokinin. This hormone causes the gallbladder to contract and expel the stored bile into the small intestine (see HORMONE).

There are several diseases that may affect the gallbladder. The most common one is the formation of gallstones. Gallstones are hard pebblelike lumps that may block the passage of bile from the gallbladder to the small intestine. If blockage occurs, the patient often has abdominal pain and may develop the condition known as jaundice. Gallstones can be removed by a surgeon, though often the entire gallbladder is removed to prevent recurrent formation of stones. Techniques are also available that smash gallstones with ultrasound (see ULTRASOUND). Some stones may also be dissolved with medication.

See also BILE; LIVER.

GALL WASP Gall wasps are tiny antlike insects belonging to the family Cynipidae. Gall wasps lay their eggs just under the surface of plants. When the eggs hatch, the larvae cause the plant tissue to swell into what are called galls (see LARVA). Although the exact reason for the formation of galls is not known, it is believed that the larvae release a chemical that causes the plant tissue in the area to grow abnormally. Inside the gall, one or more larvae feed on the nutritious new plant tissue. Gall wasps are parasites because they feed off of plants (see PARASITE). Although they take nourishment from their plant hosts, gall wasps do not seem to do any serious damage. Each species of gall wasp produces a characteristic type of gall on a specific type of plant. Although oak trees are a favorite of many gall wasps, some species prefer to attack members of the rose family or composite family.

Gall wasps are tiny. They rarely grow more than 0.25 in. [6mm] long. Most are dark brown or black and have a shiny abdomen, which is flattened on the sides. Reproduction takes place most often by parthenogenesis, which is the development of unfertilized eggs. As a result, male gall wasps are rare. Some species alternate this parthenogenetic stage

GALL WASP
Each of the swellings, called galls, on this oak tree (top) contains a larva (grub) of a gall wasp. The swellings form after a female gall wasp (above) lays her eggs in the plant's tissues.

with a sexually reproductive stage (see ALTERNATION OF GENERATIONS; PARTHENOGENESIS).

Galls can also be caused by some species of flies, aphids, beetles, moths, and mites. The galls are often preyed upon by other insects, birds, and squirrels. Theses predators eat the larvae after ripping open the gall. Some gall wasp larvae produce a bad-tasting fluid that discourages predators.

See also INSECT.

GALVANI, LUIGI (1737–1798) Luigi Galvani was an Italian doctor. He is most famous for his discovery of the connection between electricity and muscle movements.

Galvani arranged a copper wire so that it touched a leg muscle of a frog, and a silver wire so that it touched a nerve of the same frog. When the other ends of the wires were touched together, the frog's leg muscle twitched. Because of this, Galvani thought that the frog's muscle and nerve tissue had made an electric current. Although he was wrong about this, Galvani's discovery made it possible for other scientists to investigate the role of electricity in living tissue.

GALVANIZING

Galvanizing is the process of coating an article with a layer of zinc. Articles made of steel or iron are galvanized to protect them from corrosion (see CORROSION). A great many articles are galvanized, including buckets and wire fencing. Water pipes and other types of metal exposed to water are typically galvanized. About half of all the zinc mined is used for galvanizing (see ZINC).

There are several methods for coating an article

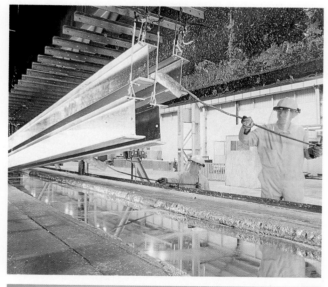

GALVANIZING

Steel girders are galvanized by being dipped in a bath of molten zinc (top). Galvanizing protects the steel railings on an open-air walkway (above) and prevents them from rusting.

with zinc. Sometimes the article is dipped in molten, or hot liquid, zinc. With this "hot-dip" method, the article is first treated to remove grease. Then it is pickled in acid to remove rust. Then it is treated with a flux, a substance that helps the zinc cling to the surface of the article (see FLUX).

Another common method of galvanizing is by electroplating. In this process, the article is placed in a solution of a zinc salt, along with some zinc. An electric current is passed through the solution from the article to the zinc. The current causes the zinc to dissolve in the solution. The zinc comes out of the solution and is deposited on the article (see ELECTROPLATING).

Zinc can be sprayed onto an article by a special tool called a metallization pistol. This pistol contains molten zinc that is sprayed out in a very fine mist. In a process called sherardizing, an article is tumbled inside a barrel with hot zinc dust. The zinc penetrates through the surface of the article. It forms an alloy with the iron inside the surface to create a coating over the surface.
See also ALLOY.

GALVANOMETER

(găl′ və nŏm′ ĭ tər) A galvanometer is a scientific instrument used to detect electric current and measure its strength. It is named for the Italian physician Luigi Galvani, who experimented with electricity in the eighteenth century (see GALVANI, LUIGI).

A galvanometer detects the magnetic field that an electric current produces. A wire carrying electricity behaves like a magnet. It attracts or repels another magnet. If the strength of the magnet's pull or push is measured, this shows how strong the electric current is. One kind of galvanometer has a coil of wire that carries the current. It is suspended between the poles of a permanent magnet. When electricity flows through the coil, the coil becomes magnetic. It twists around between the poles of the magnet. A mirror is attached to the coil. A beam of light is arranged to fall on the mirror. It is reflected along a scale. Every time the coil moves, the spot of light moves, too.

When a strong current is passing through the coil, the coil is strongly twisted. It produces a high reading on the scale. If the current is passed in the opposite direction, the coil twists in the opposite direction. Thus, the galvanometer can be used to tell which direction a current is flowing, as well as how strong it is.

See also AMMETER; ELECTROMAGNETISM.

GALVANOMETER

PROJECT 37

When an electric current flows into a galvanometer, a coil inside the instrument produces a small magnetic field. This field interacts with the stronger magnetic field of a permanent magnet, and the coil is twisted. When this happens, a mirror that is attached to the coil reflects a beam of light onto a scale. By reading this scale, the operator can measure the strength of the current.

GAMETE A gamete is a mature sex cell. In animals, male gametes are called sperm. In flowering plants and conifers, male gametes, or sperm nuclei, are produced within pollen grains. The female gametes in animals and plants are called eggs or ova (plural of *ovum*). A male gamete and a female gamete join during fertilization to form a zygote, which in turn develops into an embryo. This process of gamete union is called sexual reproduction.

In most animals and plants, gametes are formed by meiosis (see MEIOSIS). During meiosis, each gamete receives one of two sets, or half the normal number, of chromosomes possessed by normal body cells (see CELL; CHROMOSOME). Normal human cells have forty-six chromosomes and are called diploid cells. Gametes have only twenty-three chromosomes and are called haploid. When two gametes combine, the zygote gets one set of chromosomes from each gamete. Thus, the zygote has two sets of twenty-three chromosomes, for a total of forty-six, and is returned to the diploid state.

See also EMBRYO; FERTILIZATION; HEREDITY; REPRODUCTION; ZYGOTE.

GAMMA RAY A gamma ray is a high-energy electromagnetic ray of very short wavelength, similar to an X ray (see X RAY). Gamma rays are produced during the breaking down of the atomic nuclei of radioactive elements. Members of the uranium-radium series of radioactive elements give off gamma rays when they disintegrate to form new elements (see ELECTROMAGNETIC RADIATION; ELEMENT; RADIOACTIVITY).

Extremely small amounts of gamma rays bombard us from the natural activity of the things around us. When gamma rays pass through the human body, they ionize, or give electric charges to, some of the body's tissue This ionization sometimes destroys cells (see IONS AND IONIZATION). Large amounts of gamma rays are dangerous. However, these can also be of benefit. They may be used to treat some cancers, noncancerous growths, and skin problems. Medical experts also use gamma rays to examine the body for broken bones and signs of disease.

See also NUCLEAR MEDICINE; RADIATION THERAPY.

GAR The gar is a primitive freshwater fish that belongs to the family Lepisosteidae. There are five species found throughout central and much of eastern North America. The gars are long, slender fish with narrow snouts and many sharp teeth. The alligator gar may reach lengths of $11^1/_2$ ft. [3.5 m]. Gars eat other fish and are often considered a nuisance fish. They lie very still in the water and dash out to eat any fish that swims past. In some parts of the southern United States—particularly in Louisiana—fishing for gar is a popular sport. *See also* FISH.

GARLIC Garlic is a perennial plant belonging to the lily family (see LILY FAMILY; PERENNIAL PLANT). It is closely related to the onion. Garlic is native to Europe and Asia. It is cultivated throughout the world and used to flavor food. Garlic produces two types of bulbs. The underground bulbs, called garlic cloves, are the ones sold in stores. Cloves are formed at the base of the plant. Secondary bulbs, called bulblets, grow on the flower stalks of the plant and grow into new plants when they fall to the ground (see BULB AND CORM).

In ancient times, garlic was used as a good luck charm and as a drug. Its value as a medicine has been confirmed because of a substance called allium in garlic. Allium is an antibiotic that can also be used as an antiseptic.

See also ANTIBIOTIC; ANTISEPTIC.

GARLIC

Garlic cloves are underground bulbs. They are harvested when they are ripe, and hung up to dry.

GARNET Garnets are a group of hard, glassy minerals (see MINERAL). Some garnets, especially the ruby-red pyrope and the transparent almandine garnet, are semiprecious gemstones used in making jewelry. Other garnets are used as abrasives (see ABRASIVE). Garnets are found in South Africa and in Arizona and Colorado in the United States.

GARNET

The garnets in this picture are not of gem quality. Instead of being made into jewelry, they will be ground up and used as abrasives for grinding and polishing.

GARTER SNAKE A garter snake is a medium-sized snake that belongs to the family Colubridae. There are eight species of garter snakes in North America. Although some species are found only in certain areas, the eight species together are found throughout the United States. Garter snakes are very common in many areas of the country. They are often found near water. Most species grow to 26 in. [66 cm] in length. Garter snakes were so named because their colorful markings resemble fancy garter straps once used to hold up men's socks. Garter snakes eat frogs, toads, insects, and small mammals and birds. They are harmless to people. *See also* SNAKE.

GARTER SNAKE

Garter snakes are easily recognized by the pale yellow stripes running along the whole body. Garter snakes are not poisonous.

Gas, liquid, and solid are the three states of matter. In a solid, the atoms or molecules are fixed in position. In a liquid, they are free to move within limits. In a gas, the atoms or molecules are able to move wherever they can. A gas fills whatever it is put into and takes the container's shape. A gas without any container would keep expanding. On the other hand, a gas can be squeezed into a smaller and smaller container. This cannot happen with liquids or solids (see ATOM; MOLECULE; STATES OF MATTER).

The molecules of a gas are in constant motion. They move without stopping. They bounce off each other, and they bounce off the walls of their container. As they bombard the walls, they press against them. The pressure of a gas is due to the momentum of all the molecules hitting against their container walls. The behavior of gases is explained if we think of them as molecules in constant motion. This is called the kinetic theory of gases. *Kinetic* means "having to do with movement" (see KINETIC THEORY).

If a gas is compressed (squeezed) into a smaller and smaller space, the molecules have less room to move around. They hit the walls more and more often. The pressure goes up. When a certain point is reached, the molecules can hardly move at all. The gas turns into a liquid. The same thing happens when a gas is cooled—energy is taken from its molecules. They slow down and do not bounce off each other as vigorously. They get closer and closer, and the gas turns into a liquid.

Some gases can be turned into liquids just by compressing them, but many need to be cooled as well. Each gas has what is known as a critical temperature. Above this temperature, it is impossible to liquefy the gas. The critical temperature for the gas ammonia is 270°F [132°C]. Above this temperature, the gas ammonia cannot be turned into a liquid. The critical temperature for nitrogen is much lower. It must be cooled to -233 °F [-147°C] before liquid nitrogen is made. The critical temperature for hydrogen is -400°F [-240°C]. For helium, it is even lower, at -450°F [-268°C]. This is getting near the lowest temperature possible, which is -459.67°F [-273.15°C], or absolute zero (see ABSOLUTE ZERO).

To reach very low temperatures, special cooling methods must be used. Nitrogen cannot be liquefied by normal refrigeration. Instead, it is cooled as far as possible and then compressed. Then the compressed gas is allowed to expand through a nozzle. This causes cooling by what is known as the Joule-Thomson effect. The temperature falls below the critical temperature, and the nitrogen liquefies. This method will not work with hydrogen. Hydrogen is liquefied by evaporating liquid air. This produces sufficient cooling.

The Irish scientist Robert Boyle discovered the important law about gases that is named after him (see BOYLE'S LAW). It states that the volume of a gas will increase as its pressure decreases, and vice versa.

LIQUID GAS

Gases condense to form liquids if they are made cold enough. Here, liquid nitrogen, at a temperature of below -324°F [-198°C], is being poured from one flask into another. The coldness has caused water vapor in the air to form a thick frost on both flasks.

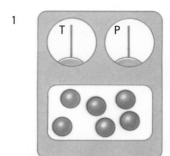

Helium, a monatomic gas

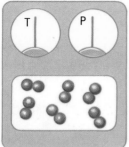

Hydrogen, a diatomic gas

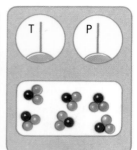

Carbon dioxide, a triatomic gas

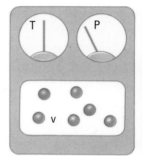

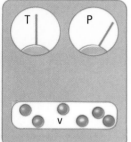

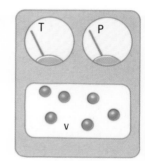

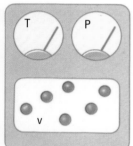

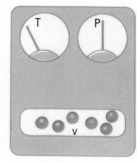

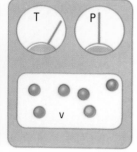

GAS LAWS

(1) Avogadro's law: At the same temperature and pressure, equal volumes of all gases contain equal numbers of molecules.

(2) Boyle's law: At constant temperature, the volume of a gas is inversely proportional to the pressure.

(3) Pressure law: At constant volume, the pressure of a gas is proportional to its absolute temperature.

(4) Charles's law: At constant pressure, the volume of a gas is proportional to its absolute temperature.

GAS DIFFUSION

Bromine forms a brown gas. Originally, bromine was in the lower jar and air was in the upper jar. The two jars were separated by a glass plate. When the plate was removed, the bromine gradually diffused (moved) from the lower jar to the upper one. After a while, both jars contained the same mixture of bromine and air.

The French scientist Jacques Charles stated another important law a century later (see CHARLES'S LAW). Charles's law states that the volume a gas occupies under constant pressure varies with its temperature.

Gases have very low densities (see DENSITY). This explains why they are poor conductors of heat and electricity. For an electric current to pass through 0.394 in. [1 cm] of dry air, a voltage of about 30,000 volts must be applied to the gap. This causes ions to form (see IONS AND IONIZATION).

Eleven of the elements are gases at room temperature. These are hydrogen, nitrogen, oxygen, fluorine, chlorine, and the six noble gases of helium, neon, argon, krypton, xenon, and radon. Pairs of atoms of the first five combine to form molecules. The molecule of oxygen can thus be written O_2 and the molecule of hydrogen H_2. They are diatomic gases. Noble gases are monatomic gases, with single atoms that do not combine to form molecules (see ELEMENT; NOBLE GAS). Air is not a single gas. It is a mixture of gases, mainly nitrogen and oxygen.

See also AVOGADRO, AMEDEO; VAPOR. **PROJECT 10**

GASOLINE

Gasoline is a thin, highly flammable liquid. It is a mixture of many different hydrocarbons (see HYDROCARBON). Gasoline is obtained from petroleum by distillation. It readily turns to vapor and is explosive when mixed with air. This makes it an ideal fuel for automobile engines (see DISTILLATION; ENGINE; PETROLEUM; VAPOR).

When petroleum is distilled, it gives only about 25 percent gasoline. At this point, the gasoline is not very high in quality. To get high-quality, or high-grade, gasoline from petroleum, other processes are used. The most important is called cracking. In cracking, heat, pressure, and catalysts (substances that speed up chemical reactions) are used. These techniques break down heavy hydrocarbons into lighter ones, suitable for use in gasoline. Gases are also produced during cracking. These gases can be turned into gasoline by the process called polymerization. (see CRACKING; POLYMER). There are several other processes that can be carried out on the petroleum products obtained by distillation. The final yield is over 50 percent high-grade gasoline.

In a gasoline engine, gasoline is mixed with air. The mixture is exploded in the automobile's cylinders. This drives the pistons. If the mixture explodes too quickly, a noise called knocking, or pinking, is heard in the engine. The engine loses power. It may also be damaged. Certain kinds of hydrocarbons called octanes are found in gasoline. They determine the gasoline's resistance to knocking. The higher the proportion of octanes, the less knocking there is. Gasolines can be graded by their octane rating.

Several substances called additives may be put into gasoline to improve it. Tetraethyl lead acts as an antiknock agent. However, because lead is highly toxic (poisonous), it has been phased out of most gasoline. Most of the cars on the road today use unleaded gasoline. Other additives prevent oxidation in the fuel storage tank (see OXIDATION AND REDUCTION). Some prevent harmful material from the gasoline from being deposited in the engine. Some additives act as lubricants. They reduce the friction between the pistons and the engine cylinders.

OIL REFINERY
Gasoline is one of the chief products of an oil refinery, which also produces other fuels such as kerosene and diesel fuel.

One problem with using gasoline in engines is that many of the hydrocarbons found in gasolines do not burn. Instead, the hydrocarbons are emitted from the engines into the air. Sunlight reacts with hydrocarbons, causing smog. The burning of gasoline also gives off carbon dioxide, carbon monoxide, and oxides of nitrogen. These substances contribute to air pollution (see AIR; POLLUTION; SMOG). Some gasoline companies are introducing reformulated fuels. Reformulated fuels have a different mixture of additives and octanes than does "normal" gasoline. These fuels burn more completely, so they give off fewer hydrocarbons.

Another problem with using gasoline is that gasoline is made from petroleum, a fossil fuel that is a nonrenewable resource (see FOSSIL FUEL). Nearly all the easily reached petroleum has been mined. Within fifty years, the world's supply of petroleum is expected to be gone. Several alternatives to gasoline have been considered, such as diesel fuel, compressed natural gas (CNG), liquid hydrogen, liquefied petroleum gas (LPG), ethanol, and methanol. There are advantages and disadvantages to each of these alternatives. For example, diesel fuel gives more power per gallon and burns more completely than gasoline, but gives off a tremendous amount of pollution. For CNG, liquid hydrogen, and LPG to be put into use, there would have to be widespread changes in service stations, fuel tanks, and fuel-processing plants. Also, hydrogen does not release harmful pollution when it burns, but it is very expensive to produce and highly explosive.

One alternative to gasoline that was once seen to have more promise than the other alternatives is gasohol, a mixture of gasoline and ethanol or methanol. Ethanol is an alcohol made from certain grains or vegetables. Methanol is an alcohol made from coal, natural gas, or wood. When ethanol and methanol are burned as fuels, they burn more cleanly, or completely, and give off fewer unburned hydrocarbons, carbon dioxide, and certain other chemicals. However, their production involves the release of large amounts of carbon dioxide. Ethanol also costs four times as much as gasoline to produce.

GASOHOL

Gasohol—a mixture of gasoline and alcohol—is a poorer fuel than gasoline on its own but causes less pollution of the air when it is burned.

Methanol can be produced relatively cheaply from coal or natural gas, both of which the United States has in abundant reserves. Methanol can also be produced using wood (see BIOMASS). Methanol can be burned in most existing automobile engines and supplied through existing service stations. However, methanol has its share of problems, too. The burning of methanol gives off a toxic chemical, formaldehyde (see FORMALDEHYDE). Scientists are searching for a method to burn or use the formaldehyde before it is released in automobile exhaust. Another problem is that methanol burns with an invisible flame, which could be very dangerous during an accident.

In spite of its environmental advantages, gasohol does not provide as much energy as gasoline. For example, a car may be able to drive twenty-five miles on a gallon of gasoline but only fifteen miles on a gallon of gasohol with ethanol and eight miles on a gallon of methanol.

Vehicles that can burn either gasoline or gasohol, called flexible-fuel vehicles, are being used in California. Fleet managers and drivers report general satisfaction with these environmentally sensitive vehicles. The new fuel in widest use is a mixture of 85 percent methanol and 15 percent gasoline.

GASTRIC JUICE Gastric juice is the mixture of digestive fluids produced by the stomach wall (see STOMACH). Its exact make-up depends on the diet of the animal. In humans, the gastric juice is a watery solution. It contains mainly hydrochloric acid and the enzymes known as pepsin and rennin (see ENZYME). The hydrochloric acid sterilizes the food by killing most of the bacteria, and provides the acidic conditions needed by the enzymes (see DIGESTIVE SYSTEM). The enzymes begin the digestion of proteins, breaking them down into simpler chemical substances. The different acids and enzymes in gastric juice are produced by different kinds of cells in the stomach wall. The flow of gastric juice is controlled by nerves and hormones and usually begins as soon as food enters the mouth. *See also* DIGESTION.

GASTROPOD The gastropods are the members of the large class of mollusks that includes the snails and slugs (see MOLLUSCA). They are often called *univalves*, meaning "one shell." Most gastropods have a single, coiled shell, though some gastropods have no shell at all. These shell-less gastropods are called slugs.

Gastropods move by means of a large fleshy or muscular foot. Snails can pull the foot back into the shell when they are alarmed or when they are resting. In many aquatic (water-dwelling) snails, there is a horny plate called an operculum at the back of the foot. The operculum fits neatly into the shell, closing like a door when the snail withdraws its body into its shell. Most land gastropods have no operculum, although they can seal the shell opening with mucus that hardens into a protective plate.

Most of a gastropod's internal organs are located in a part of the body called the visceral hump. This hump always remains inside the shell of a snail. Marine and freshwater snails breathe by means of gills that are located in a space called the mantle cavity (see GILLS). In land slugs and snails, the mantle cavity has changed into an air-breathing lung. Some freshwater snails also have lungs and they come to the surface from time to time to breathe. Sea slugs have false gills, which are fingerlike outgrowths from the body and which absorb oxygen from the surrounding water.

Some kinds of gastropods, including most land snails and slugs, have two pairs of retractile tentacles, or feelers, with eyes at the tips of the longer ones. The gastropod uses the other pair to smell, taste, and feel its way around. Most aquatic gastropods have just one pair of tentacles, with eyes at their base.

Gastropods feed by means of a radula, which is a tonguelike strip of tissue covered with horny teeth. Vegetarian gastropods, such as garden snails, have hundreds or even thousands of small, weak teeth. Carnivorous (meat-eating) gastropods have fewer teeth, but they are larger and stronger. Cone shells

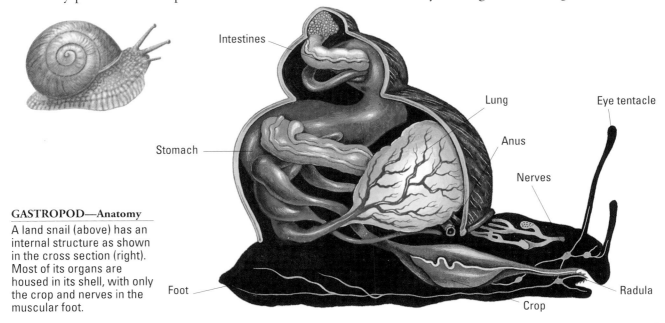

GASTROPOD—Anatomy
A land snail (above) has an internal structure as shown in the cross section (right). Most of its organs are housed in its shell, with only the crop and nerves in the muscular foot.

Intestines · Lung · Eye tentacle · Anus · Stomach · Nerves · Foot · Radula · Crop have just a few needlelike teeth that they fire at their prey like harpoons.

Most gastropods have separate male and female individuals, but some of the lung-breathing slugs and snails are hermaphrodites. This means that each animal has male and female sex organs. Some of them can fertilize themselves, but most of them still pair up and mate (see HERMAPHRODITE).

GASTROPOD—Sea slug
The sea slug is a colorful shell-less gastropod that lives on coral reefs in shallow warm seas.

GAS TURBINE
A gas turbine is a kind of internal-combustion engine. Basically, a turbine is a wheel that is turned by the force of a moving fluid. The turning wheel is mounted on a shaft. The shaft, in turn, powers a machine—such as an airplane or ship, a locomotive, or an electric generator (see ENGINE; TURBINE).

A gas turbine can use almost any kind of fuel that gives off gases when burned. Natural gas and oil are usually used in gas turbines. The important difference between a steam turbine and a gas turbine is that the energy from the burning fuel in a steam turbine must first heat water. The steam that is created from the hot water then turns the turbine wheels. In a gas turbine, the hot gases from the burning fuel turns the turbine wheels directly.

The three main parts of a gas turbine are the air compressor, the combustion chamber, and the turbine. The compressor does two things. First, it sucks in air from the outside, and then it compresses (squeezes) the air. The compressed air next passes into the combustion chamber and mixes with the fuel. The mixture of compressed air and fuel is ignited by an electric spark. The compressed, burning gases expand with tremendous force. They rush from the combustion chamber and pass through the turbine, spinning the wheels. The wheels are connected to a shaft, and the turning shaft then powers some device.

After the gases pass through the turbine, they escape through the exhaust. These exhaust gases can be used to help operate the turbine. In some gas turbines—such as those used to run an electric generator—the exhaust is used to heat the air in the compressor. That means that less fuel is needed to burn the gas in the combustion chamber. This makes the turbine more efficient. In other gas turbines—such as those used in aircraft engines—the exhaust gases are forced out of the back of the engine. This creates more forward power for the airplane.

Steam and water turbines have been in use since about 1900. Gas turbines, however, could not be built until metal alloys were developed that could withstand the heat created in the combustion chamber (see ALLOY). Engineers perfected the gas turbine in the early 1940s. Today, gas turbines are used to power land, sea, and air vehicles. They are also used in industry and in electric-power plants.

The widest use of gas turbines is in jet aircraft

GAS TURBINE—Jet fighters
F15 fighter aircraft have two powerful gas turbine engines, usually known as jet engines.

engines. Gas turbines are most efficient when they operate at full power. This makes them well suited for operation in high-speed jet aircraft (see JET PROPULSION). Gas turbines are also used in turbo-prop engines. In a turboprop engine, the gas turbine powers the propeller. In addition, however, the exhaust gases are forced out of the back of the engine, which adds to the thrust of the engine. Another use of the gas turbine in aircraft is in turbofan engines. The turbofan engine works much like a conventional jet engine, but there is a fan placed where the outside air enters the engine. The fan takes in much more air, and it also compresses the air. Most of this compressed air travels around the engine through a bypass duct. The air exits the engine at a greater speed than it had when it entered. This gives the engine extra forward power.

During the 1950s, gas turbines were used in some railroad locomotives. However, gas turbine engines are less efficient than the diesel engines used in most locomotives. Because of the relatively small size and light weight of gas turbine engines, they were adapted for use in ships in the early 1970s.

Beginning in the 1960s and continuing into the 1980s, experiments were made using gas turbines in automobiles. However, the cost of manufacturing and operation has prevented gas turbines from replacing the regular internal-combustion engine in cars and trucks.

Two applications of the gas turbine in industry are in the oil-refining process and in compressor stations along natural-gas pipelines. Most turbines in electric-power plants are steam turbines. That is because the pressure of a gas turbine is not great enough to operate a whole power plant. However, gas turbines are often used along with steam turbines to increase the efficiency of a plant. Gas turbines are also used as a standby system in a plant. They are used in portable electric-power plants, as well.

GAUSS (gous) The gauss is a unit used to measure the strength of a magnetic field (see MAGNETIC FIELD). It is named after Karl F. Gauss, a German mathematician, who did important work in electromagnetism in the 1800s. The magnetic field of the earth measures about one-half a gauss. It is believed that the magnetic field at the surface of a neutron star may be as large as several billion gauss (see NEUTRON STAR). Special superconducting magnets now being developed can produce magnetic fields of fifty thousand gauss or more.
See also ELECTROMAGNETISM; GAUSS, KARL FRIEDRICH; MAGNETISM; SUPERCONDUCTIVITY.

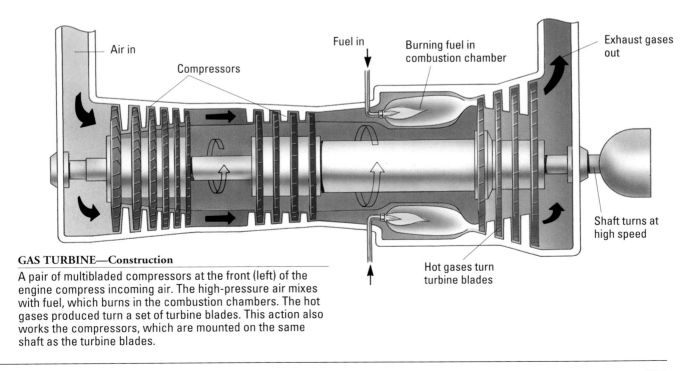

Air in

Compressors

Fuel in

Burning fuel in combustion chamber

Exhaust gases out

Shaft turns at high speed

Hot gases turn turbine blades

GAS TURBINE—Construction

A pair of multibladed compressors at the front (left) of the engine compress incoming air. The high-pressure air mixes with fuel, which burns in the combustion chambers. The hot gases produced turn a set of turbine blades. This action also works the compressors, which are mounted on the same shaft as the turbine blades.

GAUSS, KARL FRIEDRICH (1777–1855)

Karl Gauss was a German mathematician. He was born at Brunswick, the son of a poor gardener. He was so brilliant that Duke Ferdinand noticed him and paid for his education.

Gauss made his first great discovery in geometry when he was a student. Using only a straightedge and compasses, he made a seventeen-sided regular polygon. Even the ancient Greek mathematicians had not managed to do this. Gauss went on to prove that some polygons could never be drawn with only a straightedge and compasses. This was the first time anyone had proved something in geometry to be impossible. After that, proving that things were impossible became an important field of mathematics.

Gauss also became famous as an astronomer. He invented a machine called a heliotrope. This machine reflected sunlight over long distances. He used the straight lines of reflected light to measure the shape of the earth by trigonometry. Gauss worked out the positions of the earth's magnetic poles. He realized that he needed a set of units to measure magnetic effects. He developed these in 1832. At the same time, he made a study of the theory of measurement. The unit that measures the strength of a magnetic field is named for him.

See also GAUSS.

GAZELLE

Gazelles are slender, graceful antelopes. These animals are herbivores and belong to the same family (Bovidae) as cattle (see ANTELOPE; HERBIVORE). There are about twelve species, living on the dry, open grasslands of Africa and Asia. Some live in small family groups, but most gazelles live in large herds, often of several hundred animals. The name *gazelle* comes from an Arabic word meaning "affectionate." Most gazelles stand about 3 ft. [1 m] tall at the shoulder. They have large, black eyes and long, pointed ears. They are light to dark brown with a white belly and a small white tail. They often have a dark band on the side. Males generally have long, slightly curved horns, but females have just short spikes or no horns at all. The horns of most species have ringlike ridges around them.

The most common gazelles are Thomson's gazelle and Grant's gazelle, which both live in East Africa. The dorcas gazelle of the Sahara region is the smallest gazelle—only about 21 in. [53 cm] high. It was domesticated by the ancient Egyptians.

Gazelles are fast runners and often reach speeds of 40 m.p.h. [64 kph]. Gazelles are protected by law in most countries. Because of extensive illegal hunting, however, some species of gazelles are endangered and may soon be extinct.

See also ENDANGERED SPECIES.

GAZELLE

Gazelles, native to the plains of Africa and Asia, usually band together in herds. They eat only plants but are a major source of food for such meat eaters as lions and tigers.

GEAR A gear is a mechanical device that transfers power and rotating (spinning) motion from one part of a machine to another. One of the most common gears is the spur gear. It consists of a metal wheel with slots, called teeth, around the edge. The teeth of one gear are fitted into the teeth of another gear. Thus, when the first gear turns, the second gear turns with it. The gears are mounted on shafts, called axles. One axle runs to the source of power. When the power axle turns, its gear turns. This causes the second gear to turn, which makes the second axle rotate.

When gears are disconnected, the machine is said to be out of gear. Automobiles, for example, are put out of gear by moving the gearshift lever to a neutral position. This action causes the gears to move apart, and the automobile does not move even though its engine is running.

Gears usually operate in pairs. Generally, one gear is larger than the other gear. They are known respectively as gear and pinion. If the pinion, or smaller gear, is the driving member, the system acts as a speed reducer. This is because the larger gear that supplies the power to the machine turns more slowly than the small gear that is driving it. However, if the gear drives the pinion, the system acts as a speed increaser. Now, the small gear, or pinion, supplies power to the machine. It turns at a faster speed than the large gear. For example, a 30-tooth gear driving a 15-tooth pinion doubles the speed of rotation. The gear ratio is said to be 2 to 1. The difference in speed of the gear wheels changes the force transmitted. A slow-running gear rotates with greater force than a fast-turning gear. This is how an automobile in low gear generates the force to start the car moving from a standing start.

Gear and pinion turn in opposite directions when they mesh, or come together. However, if it is necessary for them both to turn in the same direction, a third gear, called an idler, is positioned between them. This arrangement is called a compound train of gears.

Another type of gear arrangement is called the rack and pinion system. This is used in automobile steering systems and in microscope-focusing mechanisms. The rack is usually a straight piece of metal with teeth. The teeth on the pinion mesh with the teeth on the rack and cause it to move in a straight line forward or backward.

Other types of gears include bevel gears, worm gears, helical gears, friction gears, and planetary gears. Bevel gears have teeth that slant at angles. They usually transfer power at right angles. Worm gears have one gear similar to a spur gear and an endless screw around one of the axles. The teeth in the spur gear mesh with the screw and cause it to turn the second shaft. Helical gears resemble spur gears, but their teeth run at an angle to the shaft,

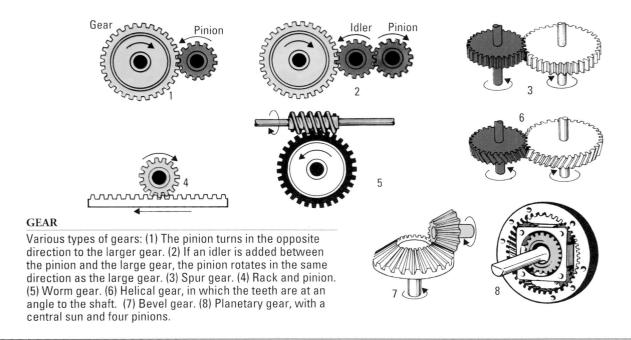

GEAR

Various types of gears: (1) The pinion turns in the opposite direction to the larger gear. (2) If an idler is added between the pinion and the large gear, the pinion rotates in the same direction as the large gear. (3) Spur gear. (4) Rack and pinion. (5) Worm gear. (6) Helical gear, in which the teeth are at an angle to the shaft. (7) Bevel gear. (8) Planetary gear, with a central sun and four pinions.

not parallel to it. Helical gears are sometimes called spiral gears.

Friction gears do not have teeth. Instead, they use a shaft-driven wheel that presses against another wheel. Friction gears do not provide as much power as toothed gears. Automobile transmissions use planetary gear systems. The system consists of planetary, or pinion, gears that rotate around a sun, or central gear, in much the same way the planets of the solar system rotate around the sun.
See also AUTOMOBILE; DIFFERENTIAL.

GECKO

A gecko is a lizard that belongs to the family Gekkonidae. It gets its name from the sound it makes. Geckos have thousands of little bristles like suction cups on their toes. These bristles allow the gecko to climb and cling to smooth rocks, trees, and even glass. The major food of a gecko is insects. This group of lizards is found all over the world in tropical and subtropical climates. They are often found in and around houses, where they are welcomed because of their fly-catching abilities. They can even walk across ceilings. Geckos have been accidentally brought aboard ships from warehouses and other buildings. This has resulted in their being taken all over the world. Five of the eight species of geckos in the United States were

GECKO

Geckos can cling upside-down, like this house gecko (below, top) in a hut in Kenya, Africa. They can even cling to glass and smooth rocks (below, right) because of minute bristles on their toes (below, left).

originally from other lands but were carried to the United States on ships.
See also LIZARD.

GEIGER COUNTER

GEIGER COUNTER (gī′gər koun′tər) The Geiger counter, also called the Geiger-Müller counter, is a device used to record and measure the presence of radioactivity (see RADIOACTIVITY). Geiger counters in use today are based on designs made by the German physicists Hans Geiger and Walther Müller in the 1920s.

The Geiger counter is usually made in the form of a thin metal cylinder enclosed in a glass tube. The tube is made in a wide range of shapes and sizes. A thin wire comes down through the middle of the cylinder. This central wire and the inner wall of the cylinder are connected to an electricity supply. The wire becomes a positive electrode. The metal wall of the cylinder serves as a negative electrode (see ELECTRODE).

If ionizing radiation, such as alpha particles, beta particles, gamma rays, or X rays, is sent into the cylinder, the air or other gas inside becomes ionized (charged) (see IONS AND IONIZATION). The ions cause an electric spark to jump from the wire to the cylinder, producing a short pulse of current. These pulses are then counted electronically. The rate of the pulse activity indicates the strength of the radioactivity. This can be read on a meter. In addition, the pulses are usually amplified (increased) and fed to a small loudspeaker in the instrument. The pulses can then be heard as a series of clicks.

Besides locating sources of radioactivity, Geiger counters are sometimes used with other devices to uncover flaws in metals and to measure the thickness of sheet materials.

Some uranium prospectors carry small Geiger counters as standard equipment. Because large

Geiger counters are too big and clumsy to be used in the field, a smaller device, called the scintillation counter, is often used instead. The scintillation counter has also replaced the Geiger counter in scientific research. A scintillation counter can measure low-level radioactivity more efficiently than the Geiger counter.

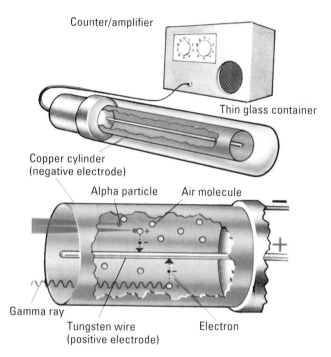

Counter/amplifier

Thin glass container

Copper cylinder
(negative electrode)

Alpha particle   Air molecule

Gamma ray

Tungsten wire   Electron
(positive electrode)

GEIGER COUNTER

A Geiger counter measures such radiation as gamma rays and alpha particles. These emissions strike molecules in the air inside the Geiger tube and cause the molecules to give off electrons. The electrons are attracted to the positive electrode, setting up an electric current that flows to a measuring instrument. Strength of radioactivity is measured as a series of clicks from an amplifier, recorded by a counter.

GEM *Gem* is a popular name for any precious or semiprecious stone, especially when it is cut, polished, and mounted as jewelry. Many minerals have

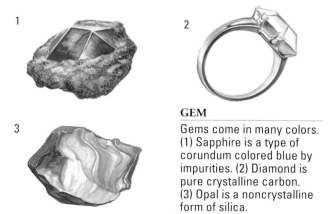

1

2

3

GEM

Gems come in many colors.
(1) Sapphire is a type of corundum colored blue by impurities. (2) Diamond is pure crystalline carbon.
(3) Opal is a noncrystalline form of silica.

gem varieties, particularly if they contain impurities that give them a slight color. For example, silica is most often found as ordinary quartz, but it also exists as the gem minerals cairngorm, cat's-eye, and opal. The dull mineral corundum becomes the gemstone ruby when it contains red impurities. This same mineral, corundum, becomes the gemstone sapphire when it contains blue.
See also AMETHYST; DIAMOND; EMERALD; RUBY; SAPPHIRE.

GENDER The gender of an animal is its sex—either male or female. Gender is determined by the genes and chromosomes in the cells (see CHROMOSOME; GENE). In humans, the cells contain 23 pairs of chromosomes. One pair is known as the sex chromosomes, called X and Y. Females have two X chromosomes in their cells, but males have one X chromosome and one Y chromosome. Some animals and most plants contain organs of both sexes and are neither male or female (see HERMAPHRODITE).
See also SEX.

GENE A gene is a unit of heredity. It determines the characteristics that an organism inherits from its parents. Each gene influences one particular characteristic, but it may take hundreds of genes to determine that characteristic completely. Genes are located on chromosomes in the nucleus of a cell (see CHROMOSOME). Each cell contains thousands of genes. Each of these genes has a specific location on one of the chromosomes. This location is called a locus.

Genes control heredity by controlling the formation of proteins within the cell (see PROTEIN). Proteins are vital to normal cell function. They form enzymes and chemical receptors, are important structural components, and serve as cellular messengers (see CELL; ENZYME). Therefore, genes control all the chemical and physical processes that take place in the development of that cell, and so determine what the cell looks like and how it behaves (see DIFFERENTIATION, CELLULAR). Genes are made of DNA. DNA carries the code for inheritance. The genes of some viruses are made of RNA.
See also DNA; GENETICS; HEREDITY; MEIOSIS; MITOSIS; MUTATION; RNA.

GENERATOR, ELECTRICAL

An electrical generator is a machine that produces electricity. Electricity is a form of energy. A generator converts movement, another form of energy known as mechanical energy, into electrical energy. It does this by making use of a relationship between electricity and magnetism. This relationship was discovered in 1831 by the English scientist Michael Faraday (see FARADAY, MICHAEL). He placed a wire between the poles of a magnet. When he moved the wire, an electric current flowed in it. The current is said to be induced in the wire. Between the poles of a magnet, there exists a magnetic field. Whenever a wire cuts through a magnetic field, a current is induced. A current can also be induced by moving the magnet and keeping the wire still. This also causes the wire to cut through the magnetic field (see ELECTROMAGNETISM; INDUCTION).

Electricity is generated in power plants. From the power plant, the electricity is sent along cables to homes and factories. The generators in a power plant are usually driven by turbines. The turbines are driven by steam or water. In most power plants,

HYDROELECTRIC POWER
Water flowing from behind a dam spins the blades of huge turbines which, in turn, power generators that produce electricity.

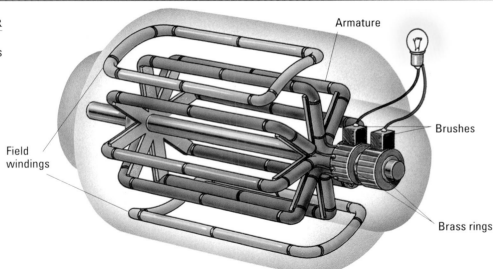

PRACTICAL GENERATOR

In a large generator, coils of wire called field windings produce a strong magnetic field. This induces an electric current in the coils of the rotating armature. The current is picked up from brass rings by a pair of carbon brushes.

Armature

Brushes

Brass rings

Field windings

the turbine causes a large coil of wire to spin around inside a magnetic field. The coil is slotted into a metal drum. Together, they are called the armature. The magnetic field is supplied by a large electromagnet. Each turn in the coil of wire produces an electric current. A large coil contains many turns. The current in each turn combines with the currents in the other turns to produce a large total current. The two ends of the coil are connected to one or two metal rings. The ring or rings are in contact with devices called brushes. The brushes are rods made out of carbon.

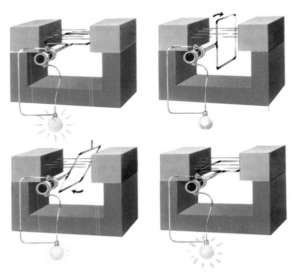

GENERATOR PRINCIPLE

This generator consists of a loop of wire rotating in a magnetic field. An electric current is induced in the wire (top left) when the wire passes through the field. When the wire is not passing through the field, no current is induced (top right). As the rotating wire reenters the field (bottom left), current again flows, reaching a maximum when the loop is at the horizontal position (bottom right).

There are two different types of electric current. They are called alternating current and direct current and are often abbreviated as AC and DC. A direct current flows in one direction only. An alternating current reverses its direction regularly. The current builds up in one direction and dies away again. Then it builds up in the other direction. Again it dies away and then builds up in the first direction again. This is called a cycle. In the United States, the alternating current in homes has sixty cycles a second.

AC generators and DC generators have slightly different designs. In both kinds, the current produced in the coil is an alternating current. As the coil spins around, any part of the coil moves first one way and then the other through the magnetic field. As the coil spins around once, one cycle of alternating current is produced. In a DC generator, the alternating current is converted into direct current.

The wires from the coil in an AC generator are connected to two rings called slip rings. In a DC generator, the wires are connected to one ring that is split in half. This split ring is called a commutator. As the coil spins, the brushes touch each half of the commutator in turn. This causes the current to reverse its direction. The current is already reversing its direction, however, because it is an alternating current. The two effects cancel each other out. The current produced flows in one direction only and is a direct current.

See also ALTERNATING CURRENT; DIRECT CURRENT.

GENETIC ENGINEERING Genetic engineering is also known as recombinant DNA technology or "gene splicing" (see DNA; GENE). It was first developed by American scientists in 1973. Genetic engineering is the process of altering hereditary material or genes in order to change some characteristic of an organism and its descendants (see HEREDITY). Genes are contained in DNA, and the chemical structure of DNA determines an organism's hereditary properties.

In genetic engineering, pieces of genetic material from one organism are transferred to another in order to change some aspect of its genetic make-up. A common application is to alter cells from organisms such as a bacteria or yeast in order to make them produce useful biological molecules such as hormones and vaccines. Genetically engineered bacteria are used to decompose forms of garbage such as oil slicks. Genetic engineering is also used to develop plants that are resistant to pests or herbicides. A new technique is being developed to try to "cure" genetically based disorders such as cystic fibrosis by using genetic engineering to "repair" the gene responsible in the affected person.

GENETIC ENGINEERING

This sheep has had a human gene inserted into its DNA. The gene causes the sheep to produce a particular protein that acts as a blood-clotting factor in humans. The protein can be extracted and used to treat humans who have a disorder caused by lack of the protein.

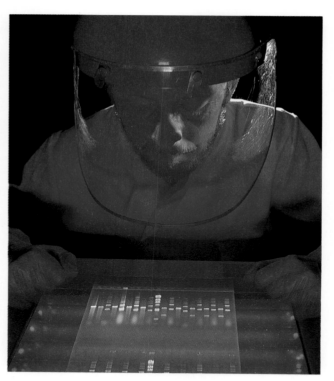

GENETIC FINGERPRINTING

A scientist studies DNA fragments by treating them with a chemical that glows with light when lit by ultraviolet light.

GENETIC FINGERPRINTING Genetic, or DNA, fingerprinting is a method of identifying individual people by examining their DNA (see DNA; GENE; GENETIC ENGINEERING). DNA fingerprinting can be used to identify a person from bloodstains, traces of saliva, root hairs, or semen. There is enough DNA to carry out fingerprinting in just one drop of blood. To make a DNA fingerprint, DNA is first extracted from the sample, then broken into fragments using a biological molecule called an enzyme. This cuts only between certain subunits of the DNA chain. Because DNA's exact structure varies from person to person, the fragments of DNA from different people are different lengths. Thus, the pattern sizes of the DNA fragments from an individual are unique, like a fingerprint. The fragments of DNA are arranged by size on a gel using an electrochemical technique to form a pattern of bands that can be photographed, or revealed using ultraviolet light. By comparing the pattern of bands produced from two different samples, it is possible to tell whether the DNA came from the same person.
See also FORENSIC SCIENCE.

Genetics is a branch of biology that deals with the nature and behavior of genes, the basic units of heredity (see GENE; HEREDITY). Genetics is concerned with the way in which certain traits, or characteristics, are passed from parents to offspring. For thousands of years, it was commonly known that animals reproduced animals like themselves and plants reproduced plants like themselves. It was known that children often looked like their parents, and that eye color, hair color, right- or left-handedness, and other physical traits were passed from parents to their children and to their children's children. Although various explanations were offered for these facts, it was not until the early 1900s that biologists really began to study heredity. Such biologists are called geneticists.

Understanding how traits pass from generation to generation is essential to the study of evolution (see EVOLUTION). An understanding of this is also helpful in order to improve the cultivation of plants and domestic animals. Geneticists have experimented with the breeding (production of offspring) of plants and animals. It has been learned that inbreeding (mating closely related males and females of the same breed) in certain species of animals can produce weak traits such as poor eyesight or stunted growth. However, outbreeding (mating with different breeds) often produces strong traits such as hardiness and resistance to disease. Some geneticists keep charts to show how specific traits pass through all members of a family line (see BREEDING).

Molecular geneticists study the physical and chemical processes responsible for inheritance. By studying the interactions of various cell components, such as chromosomes, geneticists seek to explain how individual genes reproduce themselves and how genetic "messages" are transmitted from

INHERITANCE

This little girl has inherited her mother's hair and eye color—as well as the shape of her facial features. Inherited characteristics are passed from parent to offspring by genes, which are studied in genetics.

cell to cell within a living organism. They also try to discover why abnormalities occur.

A population geneticist traces the distribution of genes in various groups. Human population geneticists trace population migrations and the intermixing of races to learn how specific traits are distributed among various groups of people.

History of genetics

Although genetics as a science did not really flourish until the early 1900s, people have long been aware of hereditary characteristics. For example, as early as six thousand years ago, Persians traced various characteristics of horses through several generations.

In 1860, Gregor Mendel, an Austrian monk, noticed that certain characteristics occurred regularly in particular species of plants and animals (see MENDEL, GREGOR). Using garden peas in his experiments, Mendel concluded that these characteristics were passed from one generation to the next. He proposed that heredity was due to small particles, which scientists later named genes. Mendel suggested two laws to explain the things he had observed. These laws, called Mendel's laws of heredity, were to become the basis of all genetics.

The first law, the law of segregation, states that small hereditary particles (genes) exist in pairs and that these pairs separate so that only one of each pair is passed from parent to child. The second law, the law of independent assortment, states that each pair of genes is inherited independently of any other pair of genes.

In 1910, Thomas Hunt Morgan, an American biologist, discovered that heredity was controlled by small structures in each cell (see MORGAN, THOMAS HUNT). Using a type of fruit fly, Morgan proved that genes were located on chromosomes (see CHROMOSOME). Morgan further proposed that since chromosomes are passed from parent to offspring, all the genes on any given chromosome are inherited together. Genes on the same chromosome are said to be linked genes. Morgan continued by showing that each gene has a specific location on a chromosome. This location is called a locus. Sometimes, during cell division when the chromosome pairs are very close to each other,

some of the genes on one chromosome will exchange with genes on the other chromosome. This is called crossing-over. Morgan proved that genes are arranged on the chromosome in a fixed linear (straight-line) order.

A few years later, Hugo De Vries, a botanist from Holland, discovered that there can be changes in some genes that cause changes in the offspring. He found that these changes, called mutations, occurred very rarely by themselves. Other scientists discovered that X rays, drugs, and other substances could be used to make mutations occur more frequently (see MUTATION).

In the 1940s, two American geneticists, George Beadle and Edward Tatum, determined that genes control the production of enzymes in the cell (see ENZYME). It is the enzymes that control all the activities of a cell by controlling its chemical reactions (see DIFFERENTIATION, CELLULAR). In 1944, Oswald Avery, another American scientist, proved that genes are made of a nucleic acid called DNA, and that DNA carries the genetic code. It is the genetic code that determines the characteristics of an organism. In 1953, James Watson and Francis Crick built a model to show the structure of DNA (see DNA; CRICK, FRANCIS HARRY COMPTON; WATSON, JAMES DEWEY). This famous double helix model further explained how DNA works. In 1966, the "genetic code" was broken, and scientists were able to predict many of the characteristics of an organism simply by studying its DNA.

Uses of genetics

Since people first planted crops and raised livestock, they have tried to improve the amount and quality of the plants and animals. For hundreds of years, a hit-or-miss method of experimentation was used to develop better varieties that were stronger, more productive, and more resistant to disease and pests. As a result, many hybrids were produced that are still popular today (see HYBRID). In more recent years, a scientific approach to breeding has greatly increased food output.

Genetic engineers use knowledge of genetics to solve problems such as disease, inadequate food production, infertility, pollution, and the need to improve breeds within species. Genetic engineering

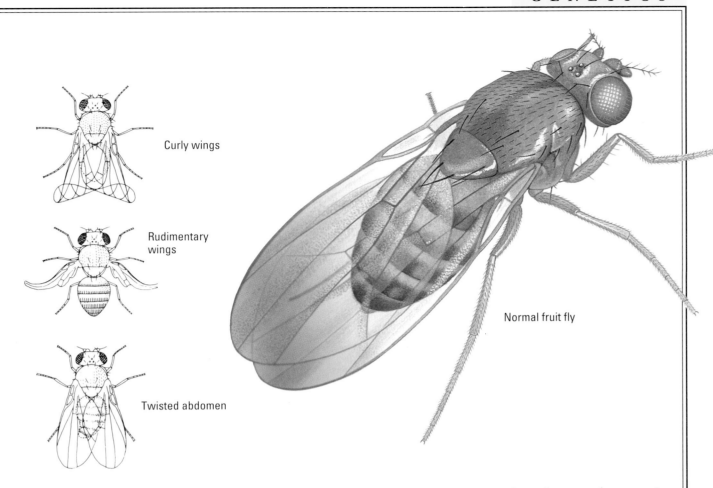

Normal fruit fly

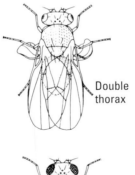

Curly wings

Rudimentary wings

Twisted abdomen

Double thorax

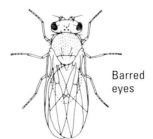

Stunted wings

Barred eyes

EXPERIMENTAL ANIMAL

The experimental animal used most often in genetic studies is the fruit fly *Drosophila*. It has a short life span and breeds easily in a laboratory. It also has very large chromosomes in its salivary glands, making them easy to see using a low-power microscope. Variations in genes on the chromosomes produce different forms of the fly. Some of these are shown (left).

is an artificial process that changes the genetic structure of an organism. The genes from one organism can be joined, or spliced, to those of another to produce specific traits. The genetic engineer does this by splitting DNA crosswise and combining it with another DNA that has also been split crosswise. This new DNA, called recombinant DNA, can then be inserted into a living system. This is a means to force one organism to take on traits of another organism. By adding DNA from certain animal cells to the DNA in bacteria cells, the bacteria produce vital animal substances such as insulin. Some of the new bacteria developed through genetic engineering are very useful. One type digests oil spills. Other experimental varieties may someday digest many other pollutants (see POLLUTION).

Exciting developments have taken place in agricultural genetic engineering. Scientists are trying to develop a self-sufficient plant. Genetic engineering techniques may soon make possible crops that resist diseases and pests, that can grow in salty soils or in very dry regions, that produce their own fertilizer, and that provide greater yields.

Other developments involve cloning. Cloning is the formation of offspring from a single parent—without sexual reproduction. The offspring, called clones, are genetically identical with each other and with the parent (see CLONE). Clones of these organisms are important for scientific research. Because the clones are identical, scientists can tell, for example, that the effects of medicines are due to the medicines, not to the differences among the organisms. Geneticists can also clone plants in order to create wanted traits, such as a certain kind of redness in apples.

Immunogenetics is the study of how genetics relates to immunity. It has led to a better understanding of how the body produces antibodies (see ANTIBODY; IMMUNITY). Geneticists have used cloning techniques to produce antibodies from human cells. The synthetic, or human-made, antibodies can then be injected into a person to improve that person's resistance to a particular disease.

Scientists are still investigating methods of cloning animals. Artificial twinning has been accomplished in animals by slicing an embryo into two or three parts and implanting the new parts into two or three different females. Cattle twins and triplets have been successfully produced in this manner.

Many people have concerns about genetic engineering. Some dangers include the possibility of harmful and uncontrollable substances being produced through cloning research that may be accidentally released into the environment. Another concern is the moral question of whether humans should interfere with nature by attempting to change the genes of living beings.

Genetic diseases

Thousands of human genetic diseases exist that afflict many people. One genetic disease, called Down's syndrome, is caused by an extra chromosome and occurs in about one out of every one thousand births. A person with Down's syndrome may be mentally retarded and usually has certain distinct physical characteristics, such as upward slanting eyes, flat nose, small head, and small, short hands. Another genetic disease, called Klinefelter's syndrome, is caused by one or more extra female sex chromosomes and occurs in about one out of every five hundred male births. The extra female chromosomes block the development of male characteristics. Klinefelter's syndrome can cause sterility, behavior disorders, or mental retardation.

Other genetic disorders can affect the heart, endocrine system, immune system, and digestive system. Genetic screening, a method that aids in determining the chances that an offspring will have certain characteristics, has greatly decreased the number of children born with genetic diseases. Genetic counselors use genetic screening to give advice to potential parents about the likelihood of their child being born with a genetic disease. Genetic screening may involve amniocentesis. In this process, fluid is removed from the amniotic sac inside a pregnant woman and examined for signs of genetic abnormality (see AMNIOCENTESIS). In spite of advancements in research, however, one out of twelve babies is born with some form of genetic disease.

The future of genetics

Genetic research is being carried out in many other areas as well. Though scientists understand the function of almost 1,500 genes, various gene-mapping projects are in progress. By the year 2005, the goal of genetic scientists is to map, or exactly locate on each strand of DNA and each chromosome, about 80,000 human genes (see GENOME PROJECT). The project, known as the Human Genome Project, is expected to cost $3 billion. Genetic scientists hope to identify as many gene codes as possible to use with genetic engineering experiments and to help predict and treat genetic disorders. Knowledge of DNA has already been used to help identify criminals. For example, cells from traces of hair, fingernails, blood, or other body tissue can furnish a DNA "print." A person's DNA print is more accurate than a fingerprint. It is so accurate that DNA identification is accepted as evidence in a court of law.

See also EVOLUTION; MOLECULAR BIOLOGY; REPRODUCTION.

GENOME PROJECT The Human Genome Project began in the United States in 1989. The aim of the project is to map, or locate, the sequence of chemical building blocks called nucleotides on a strand of human DNA. Up to 10 percent of the sequences represent genes—about 80,000 of them (see DNA; GENE; GENETICS). Similar projects were begun in Great Britain and other European countries, with research efforts focusing on different areas.

Most of the studies concentrate on either genetic mapping, physical mapping, or DNA sequencing. Genetic mapping aims to determine the relative positions of hereditary characters. When families are analyzed, if two characters are nearly always found to be inherited together, this shows that they are located "near" each other on the same chromosome. Physical mapping aims to determine the position of each gene on the chromosome. DNA sequencing shows the actual sequence of DNA bases on each chromosome. Each area is essential in defining the human genetic map. A detailed map is essential for localizing the gene responsible for a hereditary disease, for example.

GENOTYPE (jĕn′ə tīp′) The genotype of a plant or animal is its genetic make-up (see GENE). This make-up is the particular combination of genes that it inherits from its parents (see HEREDITY). This genetic make-up is not always reflected in the appearance of the organism because some of the genes that are present in the genotype may be masked by others known as dominant genes (see DOMINANCE). The cells of pea plants, for example, contain two genes controlling the height of the plants. There may be two "tall" genes, two "short" genes, or one of each. There are therefore three possible genotypes as far as height is concerned. However, there are only two phenotypes, or appearances, a pea plant can have— tall or short (see PHENOTYPE). This is because "tall" genes are dominant over "short" genes. Any plant containing a "tall" gene will be tall.

GENUS A genus, in the classification of living organisms, is a subdivision of a family. It is made up of a group of related species.
See also CLASSIFICATION OF LIVING ORGANISMS; FAMILY; SPECIES.

GEOCHEMISTRY Geochemistry is the science that applies chemistry to the study of the earth. Geochemists study the chemical composition of and distribution of elements in the earth's crust, in the atmosphere, and in the oceans. Through complex scientific methods, geochemical prospectors locate deposits of minerals and other valuable substances. Isotope geochemists are able to determine the age of rocks and meteorites. The study of geochemistry has also yielded much new knowledge about erosion, as well as about the origin of life on Earth.
See also CHEMISTRY; GEOLOGY.

GEOCHEMISTRY

A geochemist in a laboratory grinds up a sample of soil. The sample can then be analyzed. Such analysis can be used to detect contamination by poisonous heavy metals such as cadmium or lead.

GEODE Geodes are hollow mineral formations that are lined with crystals. In many cases, the crystals are quartz, such as amethyst. The crystals may also be calcite or hematite or certain other kinds of minerals (see AMETHYST; CALCITE; CRYSTAL; HEMATITE; MINERAL; QUARTZ).

Geodes are found in sedimentary or igneous

GEODE

Geodes resemble large hollow pebbles that are lined with crystalline minerals, such as quartz and amethyst. This geode has been cut open to reveal the crystals inside.

rocks (see ROCK). They form in sedimentary rock when water that is rich in minerals seeps into certain hollow spaces. Due to pressure, crystals eventually form, lining the sides of the hollow space. Geodes form in igneous rocks when hot gases cool in certain hollow spaces, forming crystals. Geodes range from the size of a grape to the size of a large pumpkin.

Geodes with well-formed crystals are prized by collectors. They are often broken open, so the crystals can be viewed.

GEOGRAPHY Geography is the science that studies the physical features of the earth and the relationship between living organisms and the earth. The field can be subdivided into other fields.

Physical geography is the study of the physical features of the earth. It is further subdivided into other fields. For example, geomorphology is the study of landforms on the earth's surface. Climatology is the study of climate (see CLIMATE; GEOMORPHOLOGY).

Biogeography is the study of the distribution of plants and animals on Earth. Human geography is an important subdivision of biogeography. It is the study of people, their environmental needs, and how they meet these needs. Political geography explores how the human race has broken itself

GEOGRAPHY

The features of a landscape, such as mountains, cliffs, and rivers, are studied in the branch of geography called physical geography.

up into units such as nations and cities.

Geography is an important field. It helps people become aware of the natural resources on Earth. Geography also emphasizes the need for conservation. It helps people realize that they need to use the environment without abusing it.

See also GEOLOGY; MAP AND MAPPING.

GEOLOGICAL MAP

A geological map shows the kinds of rocks found in a given area. There are two main kinds: a "drift" map shows the surface soil; and a "solid" map shows the rocks beneath, along with the angles at which they lie and any structures that they may have, such as faults (see FAULT; ROCK).

There are other kinds of geological maps, too. These include tectonic maps that concentrate on the structural details, such as the folds and faults; facies maps that plot the extent and details of a particular rock bed, whether it is at the surface or buried; and paleogeographic maps that show the geography of the area at the time a particular rock layer was deposited.

Geological maps can be used to find such valuable resources as minerals and water-bearing rocks. Modern techniques such as satellite photography can speed up the compilation of geological maps.

See also MAP AND MAPPING.

GEOLOGICAL TIME SCALE

The geological time scale is a system of classifying ages in the development of the earth. In the late 1700s and early 1800s, geologists started to study a type of rock called sedimentary rock. Sedimentary rocks are formed by material collecting at the bottom of lakes, rivers, and seas. This material is called sediment. The material gradually builds up, and the rock becomes thicker as time goes on. Early geologists studied sediment forming at the bottom of lakes and rivers. They noticed that the process happened very slowly. Some sedimentary rocks are thousands of feet thick, indicating that they must be extremely old. From this, scientists have determined that the earth is much older than they once thought.

In the early 1800s, a British engineer called William Smith discovered a law of geology. This was the law of superposition. In most sedimentary rocks, the sediment is deposited in layers. These layers are called strata. The law of superposition says that the older strata lie beneath the younger strata. The law only works for sedimentary rocks that have not been disturbed. Smith also discovered a way of comparing the ages of rocks. He did this by examining certain fossils in the rocks. Fossils are the remains of ancient plants and animals. There are many different kinds of fossils. Some fossils are found in several layers of a sedimentary rock. Other fossils are found in only one layer of a sedimentary rock. These kinds of fossils are called index fossils. Index fossils are remains of species that lasted a relatively short time on the earth. This is why they are only found in one layer of a sedimentary rock. If two different rocks contain the same index fossil, then they must be about the same age (see FOSSIL; SEDIMENTARY ROCK; STRATIFICATION).

Using Smith's method, geologists began to classify rocks in order of their ages. This led to the geological time scale. In this scale, the history of the earth is divided into eras, periods, and epochs. Geologists in the nineteenth century were unable to determine the ages of rocks. They only knew whether a rock was older or younger than another rock. Some geologists tried to calculate the ages of rocks and the age of the earth itself. For example, some tried to calculate how long it takes for a sedimentary rock to build up. These methods were all very inaccurate, and the guesses were far too low.

At the end of the nineteenth century, radioactivity was discovered. One radioactive substance is the metal known as uranium. Physicists discovered that uranium decays into lead. Uranium occurs in certain minerals. These minerals also contain lead, which is decayed uranium. Scientists compared the amounts of uranium and lead in these minerals. This enabled them to calculate more accurately the age of the minerals. Other radioactive elements can be used to determine the ages of other rocks and minerals. The oldest rocks are now known to be 4,000 million years old. The earth itself is about 4,550 million years old.

See also DATING; GEOLOGICAL TIME SCALE, VOL. 23; RADIOACTIVITY.

GEOLOGY

Geology is the study of the earth. It is the oldest of the earth sciences. It requires a knowledge of physics, chemistry, mathematics, and biology. Geology has many specialized branches. All of these branches deal with the study of the earth's crust. They are concerned with the physical history of the earth, the rocks of which the earth is formed, and the physical effects that are always changing the earth's surface. Geology is divided into two main areas—physical geology and historical geology.

Physical geology Physical geology is the study of the materials that make up the earth. It deals with the arrangement of rocks and minerals and their formation and changes. It is concerned with landmasses, ocean basins, mountains, volcanoes, and earthquakes. Its specialized branches include petrology (the study of rocks), mineralogy (the study of minerals), and sedimentology (the study of sediments and sedimentary rocks).

Other specialties of physical geology include structural geology, which concentrates on rock structures, and tectonic geology, which studies the origin of mountains. Geomorphology investigates how the surface of the earth is shaped into hills, valleys, and other landforms. Submarine geology studies aspects of the ocean floor. Geochemistry specializes in the study of the earth's chemical composition. Geophysics investigates what goes on

GEOLOGICAL TECHNIQUES

Geologists use various methods to study the earth. (1) The simplest and easiest technique involves using a hammer to chip away samples of rock. (2) Holes may be bored down through various layers of rock (strata), particularly in the search for fossil fuels such as coal and oil. (3) Small artificial earthquakes are produced by explosives. (4) The shock waves are picked up by an array of dectectors. Such seismic tests allow geologists to map the layers of rock. (5) Aerial surveys use cameras to photograph the landscape below, and instruments to measure gravity and magnetic fields. (6) Orbiting satellites can also be used for mapping the land and the oceans, either using cameras or reflected radar signals.

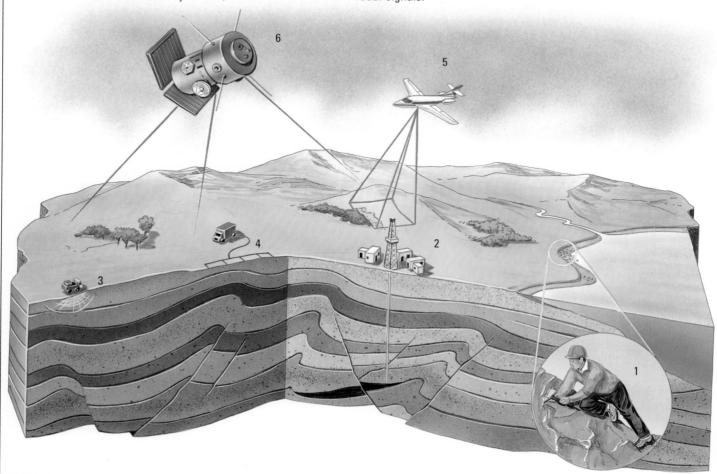

ROCKS AND STRATA

Erosion by running water has exposed layers of rock, called strata, in Horseshoe Canyon (above), located in Canada's badlands in Alberta. The rock known as schist (left) is made up of flaky plates with embedded minerals.

Scientists who study fossils are called paleontologists (see PALEONTOLOGY). By using methods of dating, paleontologists can estimate the age of fossils, thus determining the relative age of the strata in which the fossils are found. The absolute age of rocks is determined by geochemists. Geologists have divided the earth's history into a series of time periods, called the geological time scale (see GEOLOGICAL TIME SCALE).

Historical geology also includes paleoclimatology (the history of the earth's climate) and paleoecology (the study of the relationship between ancient organisms and their environment).

The history of geology The ancient Greeks were the first people to study geology. Although their studies were mixed with superstition and myth, they made some accurate observations. The Greeks realized that water is an important factor in erosion. They also believed that fossils are evidence of past life.

Geological study stopped for about one thousand

inside the earth. This specialty includes the study of magnetism and the study of earthquakes, called seismology (see GEOCHEMISTRY; GEOMORPHOLOGY; GEOPHYSICS).

Historical geology Historical geology concerns the history of the earth. Historical geologists study stratigraphy, which is the sequence of strata, or rock layers (see STRATIFICATION). Within the strata are fossils. Fossils are evidence of ancient life on Earth. The study of fossils is called paleontology.

years following the fall of the Roman Empire. During the 1500s and 1600s, Europeans gradually became interested in geology again. During this time, the Polish astronomer Copernicus and the Italian astronomer Galileo made important contributions to the study of the physics of the earth (see COPERNICUS; GALILEO).

During the 1700s, geology emerged as a modern science. A great dispute arose about the formation of rocks. One group of people, called the Neptunists, believed that the rocks of the earth's crust were all deposited from the oceans. The other group, called the Plutonists, correctly recognized igneous rock as having been formed by the cooling of molten rock within the earth (see MAGMA; ROCK). James Hutton, the leader of the Plutonists, also thought that the changes occurring on Earth had been going on throughout the earth's history. This belief is called the theory of uniformitarianism.

The earth of the twentieth century has become an exciting object of study for modern geologists. With all the tools of advanced technology at their disposal, geologists have been able to probe the earth's secrets as never before. Improved instruments, computers and calculators, communications equipment, and detectors have greatly aided field and laboratory work. Many kinds of safe and relatively comfortable transportation facilities have enabled geologists to travel to areas of study—even to the bottom of the sea.

During the middle of the twentieth century, the discovery of the Oceanic Ridge, a chain of sea mountains, excited earth scientists, including submarine geologists. This chain extends 40,000 mi. [64,360 km] around the earth. Equally exciting was the emergence of the plate tectonics theory. According to this theory, a dozen or so major plates of the earth's crust, topped with landmasses and oceans, are adrift on the softer interior of the earth. These plates, once part of a single large plate, have been slowly drifting away from or against one another (see PLATE TECTONICS). Exploration of the polar ice caps, the study of moon rocks, and the search for new energy sources all offer fresh fields of discovery for modern geologists.
See also EARTH; GEOGRAPHY.

VOLCANIC ERUPTION

Geologists study volcanoes and try to predict when they will erupt, so that local people can be warned of the danger.

GEOMETRY

Geometry is the study of different kinds of figures and their properties. It is also the study of how shapes, angles, and distances are related.

Geometry is one of the oldest branches of mathematics. The ancient Egyptians were among the first to discover geometrical properties. Every year, the Nile River overflowed its banks and flooded the countryside. The Egyptians learned to use geometry to find the boundaries of their farms after landmarks had been covered up or washed away.

The ancient Greeks began to study theoretical geometry—that is, to apply basic ideas or statements to various geometrical shapes. A man named Euclid is given the most credit for making geometry a science. About 300 B.C., he collected all the geometric results then known. He put them into a logical form in a series of thirteen books called *The Elements*. Euclid began by stating five postulates—things that seemed apparent or obvious and so were accepted without proof. The postulates were:

1. A straight line can be drawn from any point to any other point.
2. A finite straight line (a straight line of any known length) can be extended to any length in either direction.
3. A circle can be drawn with any point as center and with any radius (distance from the center to the outside).
4. All right angles are equal to each other.
5. Given a straight line and a point not on that line, there is one and only one line that can be drawn through the point that will be parallel to the given line. (Parallel lines are lines in the same plane, or flat surface, that do not meet, however far they go in either direction.)

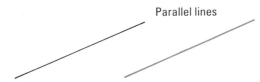

Parallel lines

Beginning with these postulates, Euclid built what is known as Euclidean geometry. Each result, or theorem, is reasoned through step by step.

Elementary geometry is chiefly concerned with shapes on a flat surface or plane. This is called plane geometry. Solid geometry uses similar rules or principles in working with solids, or three-dimensional figures. In all geometry, the basic ingredients are points and lines. From points and lines, angles can be found. An angle is the space between two lines that meet.

The Babylonians divided a complete turn into 360 equal parts called degrees. A one-quarter turn, or 360 divided by 4, is equal to 90 degrees (90°). A one-quarter turn is called a right angle. An acute angle is an angle less than 90°. An obtuse angle may range between 90° and 180°. A reflex angle is an angle greater than 180°.

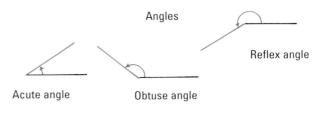

Angles

Reflex angle

Acute angle

Obtuse angle

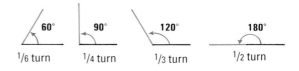

| 60° | 90° | 120° | 180° |
| 1/6 turn | 1/4 turn | 1/3 turn | 1/2 turn |

Triangles In plane geometry, the simplest straight-sided figure is the triangle. A triangle has three sides and therefore three angles. If a triangle is cut out of a piece of thick paper and the corners are torn off, the pieces that were torn off can be fitted together to make a shape with one straight edge. This shows that the angles of a triangle add up to 180°.

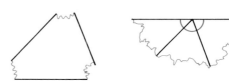

Three important triangles are the equilateral triangle, the isosceles triangle, and the right triangle. In an equilateral triangle, all the sides are the same length, and all the angles are equal. In an isosceles triangle, two sides are of equal length, and the angles opposite those sides are also equal. In a right triangle, the sides and angles are related as in the Pythagorean Theorem. This theorem states that the square of the hypotenuse (the side opposite the right angle) of a right triangle is equal to the sum of the squares of the other two sides (see PYTHAGOREAN THEOREM).

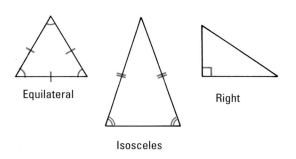

Equilateral

Right

Isosceles

Triangles and other closed figures with straight sides are called polygons. The sum of the angles of other polygons can be found by dividing them into triangles:

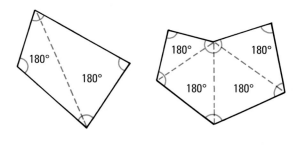

To find the sum of the angles of any polygon, count the number of sides. Subtract 2 from that number, and multiply by 180°.

If two triangles are the same shape and size, they are called congruent triangles. This property is often used to prove various theorems. To show that two triangles are congruent, it is necessary to prove any one of the following sets of conditions:

1. The three sides of one triangle are equal in length to the three sides of the other triangle (SSS):

2. Two sides of one triangle and the angle included between them are equal to the corresponding parts of the other triangle (SAS):

3. Two angles and a side of one triangle are equal to the corresponding parts of the other triangle (ASA):

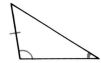

Once it has been proved that two triangles are congruent, it is then known that all the sides and angles of one triangle are equal to the corresponding parts of the other triangle. If two triangles are the same shape but are not the same size, they are called similar triangles. One triangle is larger than the other. However, the angles of one triangle are equal to the angles of the other.

If the length of XY is double that of AB, then YZ is double BC, and ZX is double CA. In geometry, this may be written XY/AB = YZ/BC = ZX/CA. Each of the corresponding ratios are equal.

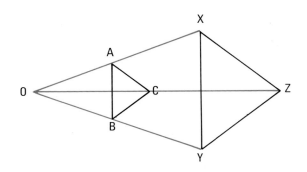

A knowledge of similar triangles is useful in surveying. Suppose it is necessary to find the height of the tree XY. A stick AB is placed so that the top of the tree can be sighted along a line from the eye to the top of the stick:

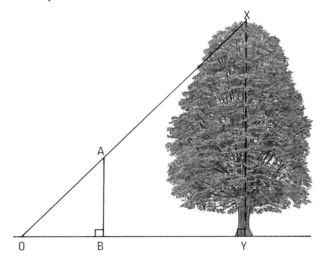

SIMILAR TRIANGLES

Similar triangles are often used in surveying. This diagram shows the setup for finding the height of a tree (see article text for explanation).

The triangles OAB and OXY are similar. Therefore, XY/AB = OY/OB. The lengths OY and OB can be measured easily. If OB = 3.3 ft. [1 m], OY = 33 ft. [10 m], and the stick AB is 3.3 ft. [1 m] in length, then XY/1 = 10/1. Therefore, XY = 33 ft. [10 m].

GEOMETRIC SHAPES

Geometry has many practical applications. Notice the triangles and other geometric shapes that are a part of these towers carrying electric cables.

Circles A circle is a closed curve on a plane. There are 360 degrees in a circle. All points on the curve are the same distance from the center.

The outer curve of a circle is called the circumference.

Circumference

The distance from the center to the circumference of a circle is called the radius.

Radius

A straight line between two points on the circumference of a circle is called a chord.

Chord

A chord that goes through the center of a circle is called the diameter.

Diameter

The formula for the area of a circle is: $A = \pi r^2$. *Pi* is a Greek letter that is written π. *Pi* stands for the number by which the diameter of a circle must be multiplied to obtain the circumference. *Pi* does not have an exact decimal equivalent, but a common estimate is 3.14.

If each angle of a triangle is bisected (cut into two equal parts), the lines doing the bisecting are concurrent. They meet at a point called the incenter (I). A circle, touching all three sides of the triangle, can be drawn with its center at the incenter. This circle is called an inscribed circle.

See also FRACTAL; POLYGON AND POLYHEDRON; SYMMETRY.

GEOMORPHOLOGY (jē'ō môr fŏl'ə jē)

Geomorphology is the study of the origin, development, and present state of the landforms (surface features) on the earth. Two groups of forces are largely responsible for the landscape of the earth: internal forces and external processes.

Internal forces originate from within the earth. They cause volcanoes, earthquakes, and faults. They are responsible for the uplifting of mountain ranges and for the movement of the plates that form the earth's crust (see PLATE TECTONICS). External processes act on or near the earth's surface and are largely responsible for erosion. These include wind, rain, and bodies of water. For example, the Grand Canyon was formed by erosion from the Colorado River. Many areas were shaped by glaciers during the ice age (see EROSION; GLACIATION). Rocks and rock formations also affect landforms.

See also GEOLOGY.

GEOMORPHOLOGY

Columns of limestone formed by erosion stand at Sunset Point in Bryce Canyon, Utah. Geomorphology studies how such features are formed.

GEOPHYSICS

Geophysics applies the laws of physics to the earth. It includes the physics of the earth's interior and exterior, as well as the physics of the atmosphere and the oceans (see PHYSICS).

Geophysicists learn about the interior of the earth through seismology. Seismology is the study of earthquakes. Seismology is closely related to volcanology, the study of volcanoes (see SEISMOLOGY; VOLCANO). Other geophysical fields include glaciology (the study of the properties of glaciers), meteorology (the study of the atmosphere and weather), and climatology (the study of climate) (see CLIMATE; GLACIATION; METEOROLOGY). Geophysicists are also concerned with the earth's magnetic field. It has been determined by scientists that the earth's magnetic field has undergone several changes in the past. These changes brought about the field of paleomagnetism, which studies the magnetism of the earth in the past (see MAGNETISM).

Through the study of geophysics, scientists have devised complex but efficient methods for locating deposits of oil, coal, and other valuable natural resources (see PROSPECTING). Scientists also try to predict volcanic eruptions by studying the pressure and temperature within an active volcano.

See also GEOLOGY.

GERANIUM

Geranium is a genus of about 400 herbaceous plants belonging to the family Geraniaceae. Most are perennial or biennial (see BIENNIAL PLANT; HERBACEOUS PLANT; PERENNIAL PLANT). They grow throughout the world in temperate areas. They are popular garden plants in the United States and Canada. Geraniums have lobed leaves and saucer-shaped flowers with five purple, white, or blue petals. Geraniums are often called cranesbills because the pistil looks like a bird's beak (see FLOWER). The most widely cultivated species, the European meadow cranesbill, reaches a height of 2 ft. [60 cm]. Another species, herb Robert, has roots that are used to make various medicines.

The name *geranium* is also given to the 250 species of the genus *Pelargonium* of the same family. Most of these plants come from tropical areas, especially from South Africa. They are often shrublike or climbing plants with clusters of brightly colored flowers, and they are very popular houseplants. The rose geranium produces geranium oil. Geranium oil is used to flavor jellies and to add scent to perfumes and cosmetic powders.

Members of a third genus, *Erodium,* in the same family, are also called geraniums. These plants are usually grown as grazing food for livestock in parts of North America and Australia. They are also known as storksbills.

GERANIUM
The popular houseplants known as geraniums are actually types of pelargoniums, valued for their colorful flowers and sometimes fragrant leaves.

GERBIL The gerbil, or sand rat, is any of about a hundred species of light brown, mouselike mammals belonging to the family Cricetidae of the order Rodentia (see RODENT). Gerbils have long hind legs that they use to jump from place to place. Most gerbils are less than 6 in. [15 cm] long, with a tail of about the same length.

Wild gerbils live in colonies, or groups, in the deserts of Africa and Asia. They burrow into the ground and often dig elaborate tunnels. Although most are nocturnal, some look for food during the day (see NOCTURNAL BEHAVIOR). Gerbils are omnivores and eat roots, nuts, grass, and insects. Some species even eat eggs and young birds. They can survive for long periods of time with little water (see OMNIVORE).

Gerbils are often considered pests because they destroy large amounts of crops in the wild. Gerbils reproduce quickly, a fact that adds to the problem. A female gerbil may give birth to four or five young as often as once a month. One genus of African gerbils, *Tatera,* is thought to be a carrier of bubonic plague. Gerbils are easy to raise and make interesting pets. The most commonly kept species is the Mongolian gerbil, which has shorter back legs than most other gerbils and does not jump as much.

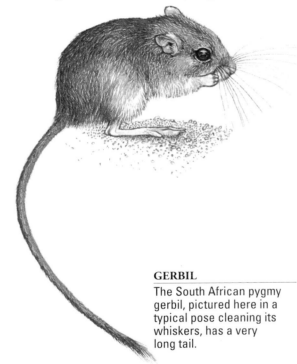

GERBIL
The South African pygmy gerbil, pictured here in a typical pose cleaning its whiskers, has a very long tail.

GERM *Germ* is the common name for any microorganism, especially one that causes disease. A germ is sometimes called a microbe. Although germs vary in size, none can be seen without the use of a powerful microscope. There are many kinds of germs, including bacteria, rickettsiae, viruses, certain protozoans, and some kinds of fungi, among other microorganisms. The scientific term for *germ* is *pathogen,* meaning "disease causer."

The word *germ* may also mean "a seed, bud, or offshoot," but the terms *germ cell* and *gamete* are used more often for this description.

See also BACTERIA; DISEASE; FUNGUS; INFECTION; MICROORGANISM; PATHOGEN; PROTOZOA; RICKETTSIA; VIRUS.

GERMANIUM Germanium is an element with a dark gray color (see ELEMENT). It looks like a metal, but it has nonmetallic properties. It is usually classified as a metalloid, not as a true metal.

Germanium is a very useful element. It is a semiconductor. It is widely used in transistors (electronic devices that control the flow of electricity), rectifiers (devices that convert alternating current into direct current), and microchips (see INTEGRATED CIRCUITS). Germanium has to be very pure for use in transistors. It is refined by the process called zone refining. Germanium is also used to make alloys for precision castings (see ALLOY; SEMICONDUCTOR).

Germanium is found in the minerals argyrodite, tantalite, germanite, and zinc blende. It was discovered in 1886 by the German chemist Clemens Winkler. He named it for his country. Germanium has the chemical symbol Ge. Its atomic number is 32, and its relative atomic mass is 72.59. It melts at 1,756°F [958°C] and boils at 5,162°F [2,850°C].

GERMAN MEASLES German measles, also called rubella or three-day measles, is a disease caused by a virus. Rubella, along with measles (rubeola), whooping cough, mumps, and chicken pox, is called a childhood disease because most people have the disease before they become adults.

German measles can be spread by coughing or sneezing. If another person breathes the virus, symptoms may appear between two and three weeks later. The most common symptoms are runny nose, low fever, sore throat, and a pink rash of raised spots that starts on the face and spreads to the rest of the body. Sometimes, no symptoms appear. The virus can be spread from a week before the rash appears to four days after it appears. In the United States, the highest outbreak of German measles occurs in May and June. Generally, no treatment is given. However, a person who gets the disease will then be immune to the virus. Since 1969, a vaccine for German measles has been available. Most doctors encourage mothers to have their babies vaccinated for rubella at age 15 months, and may encourage all girls between 10 and 14 years to

be immunized if they are not already immune. Women who are pregnant or about to become pregnant should not have the vaccine because it may cause birth defects.
See also IMMUNITY; MEASLES; VACCINATION; VIRUS.

GERMINATION Germination is the name given to the early stages of a plant's growth, from the time the seed springs into life until the young plant is able to make its own food (see PHOTOSYNTHESIS). Some seeds start to germinate almost as soon as they fall from their parent plants, but most of them have to go through a period of rest or dormancy before they can germinate (see DORMANCY). Many have to experience a period of cold and then a rise in temperature before they can germinate. This ensures that seeds scattered in the fall do not sprout until the spring, when conditions are favorable for continued growth. Dormancy can last for several years if the conditions for germination are not met. Poppy seeds, for example, can survive deep in the soil for more than 100 years. High levels of carbon dioxide and shortage of oxygen prevent germination. Some seeds contain germination inhibitors (substances that keep the seeds from germinating) in their coats, and cannot germinate until there has been enough rain to wash out the inhibitors.

GERMINATION

The hypogeal germination of a corn seed is pictured below. The radicle develops into the root. A protective sheath, called the coleoptile, forms around the plumule. Foliage leaves grow out of the coleoptile. The pericarp is the covering of the seed.

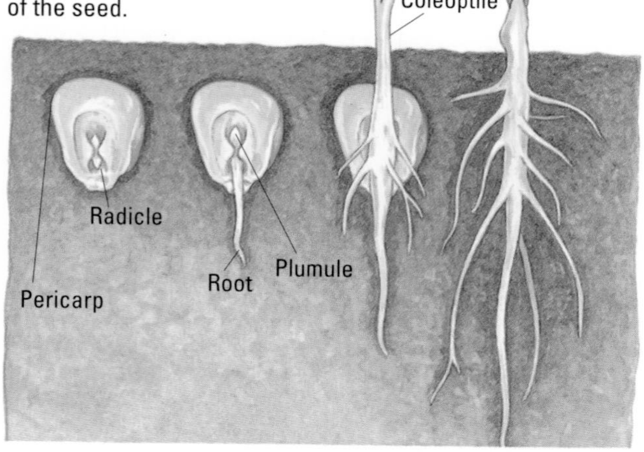

Foliage leaves

Coleoptile

Radicle

Pericarp

Root

Plumule

The main requirements for germination to begin are warmth, moisture, and oxygen—so gardeners' seeds will not grow if they are sown before the soil has had a chance to warm up in the spring, and they will not germinate in their packets either. Some seeds need light as well and will not germinate if they are sown too deeply in the soil.

When conditions are right, the seed coat softens and the embryo inside begins to grow. The embryo consists of a radicle, a plumule, and one or two cotyledons or seed leaves (see COTYLEDON; SEED). It gets its energy from food stored in or around the cotyledons. The radicle is the first thing to burst through the seed coat. It turns downwards and forms the first root. Germination then follows one of two paths. In hypogeal germination the cotyledons stay below ground and just the plumule grows up into the air to form the first shoot. This kind of germination is found in peas and broad beans. In epigeal germination the cotyledons grow up into the air, where they turn green and make food for a while. The plumule grows up between them and soon produces the true leaves. These take over the food-making process and the cotyledons wither away. Epigeal germination is found in cabbages and lettuces and many other garden plants.   PROJECT 72

GERONTOLOGY AND GERIATRICS

Gerontology (jĕr´ən tŏl´ə jē) is the study of aging, or growing old. Scientists who study the aging process are called gerontologists. They may be biologists who study the bodily changes involved with aging, psychologists who study the mental changes that accompany aging, or sociologists who study the changing relationships between aging people and the rest of society. Gerontology generally recognizes that as the bodies of humans and other animals age, the cells, tissues, and organs gradually lose efficiency. After about age forty in humans, the ability to see, hear, taste, smell, and move may diminish. Hair may begin to turn gray. Bones may lose calcium and become brittle, especially in women. The immune system may become weaker. A person may lose control of his or her bladder. Illnesses that affect the mind, such as Alzheimer's disease, may occur (see ALZHEIMER'S DISEASE). The eventual, natural result of aging is death. For women, the major biological change related to aging is menopause. Menopause occurs when the body stops releasing eggs, which are female reproductive cells (see MENSTRUAL CYCLE). Changing levels of chemicals known as hormones may cause sudden periods of body warmth, sleep disturbances, and mood changes as part of menopause (see HORMONE).

Geriatrics (jĕr´ē ăt´rĭks) is the medical practice of prevention and treatment of disease in older people. Geriatrics is gaining in importance as the number of older people in the United States increases. Today, over 12 percent of the people in the United States are over age sixty-five, and the average age of the population is steadily increasing. Geriatric specialists are now trained in many medical colleges. Besides studying the disorders of old age, they also study the bodily changes that occur in middle age, which might later lead to disease. Some of these changes occur in everyone and are considered hereditary. Other changes happen as a result of environment or preventable disease. Some scientists believe that someday the aging process may be stopped or at least slowed. Studies have shown that some diseases associated with aging, such as heart disease, can be prevented through certain dietary practices and exercise. However, many questions remain as to what causes or prevents aging.

GERONTOLOGY AND GERIATRICS
Gerontologists (scientists who study aging) help elderly people come to terms with growing old. Geriatrics is concerned with disorders that may affect elderly people.

GESTATION PERIOD In mammals, the gestation period is the time between fertilization and birth. It is the length of time that a female is pregnant (see MAMMAL; PREGNANCY). During the gestation period, the embryo grows and develops in the mother's uterus (see EMBRYO).

The length of the gestation period varies from species to species. In general, large mammals give birth to one offspring and have long gestation periods. An elephant, for example, has a gestation period of 20 to 22 months. Smaller mammals generally give birth to litters (groups of young) and tend to have shorter gestation periods. The Virginia opossum, for example, has a gestation period of only 12 days, the shortest of any mammal. Rabbits have a gestation period of 30 days. Dogs have a gestation period of about 2 months.

Evolution has adjusted the gestation periods of various animals to meet their needs. Animals that mate once a year will usually be pregnant at a time of year when food is available and the weather is favorable. For example, horses mate in the spring, have an 11-month gestation period, and give birth the following spring. Sheep mate in the fall, have a 5-month gestation period, and also give birth in the spring.

Animals that live in the open tend to have longer gestation periods than those that live in caves or burrows. This allows the offspring to continue developing and to be born in a more mature state, increasing their chances for survival. Marsupials, such as the kangaroo and opossum, have short gestation periods, but the young stay in the pouch, where they continue to grow and develop. Many scientists consider the time spent in the pouch as an extension of the gestation period (see MARSUPIAL).

By mating livestock at the same general time of the year, all of a farmer's livestock will go through gestation at approximately the same time. This has economic and other advantages for the farmer.

In human beings, the normal gestation period is about 9 months, or 267 days. This period varies, however, by as much as 3 weeks. The gestation period for male babies is about 4 days longer than for female babies. The gestation period for twins is about 6 days shorter than normal.
See also REPRODUCTION.

GIANT SEQUOIA The giant sequoia is the largest of all trees. It is an evergreen conifer and it has very thick, spongy bark (see CONIFER; EVERGREEN). It grows in forests on the western slopes of the Sierra Nevada mountains in California. The largest giant sequoia is the General Sherman tree. It is located in Sequoia National Park in central California. It measures 32.3 ft. [9.8 m] in diameter and 101.5 ft. [30.9 m] in circumference at the base. It is 272.4 ft. [83 m] tall and weighs about

GESTATION PERIOD

Gestation periods of mammals vary widely. For a rat it is up to 25 days and for a dog up to 63 days. Chimpanzees have a gestation period of about 240 days, nearly as long as a human (267 days). An elephant has the longest gestation period, from 600 to 660 days.

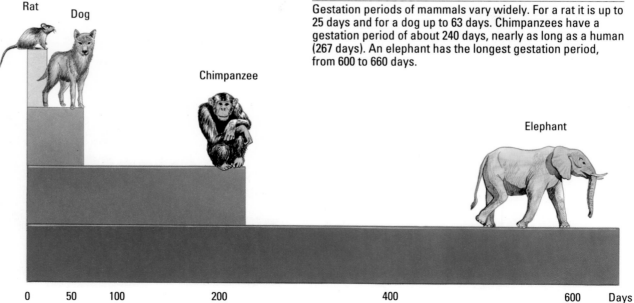

Rat   Dog

Chimpanzee

Elephant

0   50   100   200   400   600   Days

12,334,000 lb. [5,596 metric tons]. Some other giant sequoias are taller, though their trunks are not as thick. The tallest reach heights of almost 330 ft. [100 m].

Studies using radiocarbon dating and annual rings show the oldest giant sequoia stumps to be about four thousand years old (see ANNUAL RING; DATING). The giant sequoia is also called big tree, mammoth tree, and sierra redwood. It belongs to the same family as the redwood although it belongs to a different genus (see REDWOOD).

GIANT SEQUOIA
The largest giant sequoias are estimated to be four thousand years old, making them the oldest living things on Earth.

GIANT STAR Giant stars are stars much bigger and brighter than the sun. The sun is a star of average size, having a diameter of about 865,000 mi. [1,392,000 km]. Giant stars reach up to 2 billion mi. [3 billion km] in diameter.

Stars produce their energy by converting the element hydrogen to the element helium (see FUSION). When about 12 percent of the hydrogen in a star has been converted to helium, the star expands, and becomes bigger, brighter, and hotter. At this stage, the star is called a giant and may be red, blue, yellow, or orange.

The stars Aldebaran and Arcturus are orange giants. Some giants become so huge that they are called supergiants. The blue supergiant Rigel is fifty thousand times brighter than the sun. Betelgeuse in the constellation Orion is a red supergiant. It varies in size, sometimes reaching a maximum diameter of 400 million mi. [640,000 million km]. Epsilon Auriga is the largest known star, with a diameter of 2 billion mi. [3 billion km]. *See also* STAR.

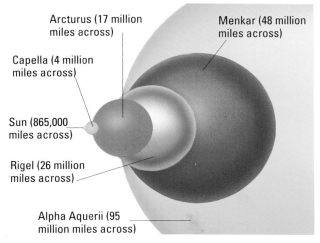

GIANT STAR
Stars expand as their hydrogen "fuel" is used up. Usually, their color changes from yellow, through orange and blue, until they become red giants. At this stage they are about 25 times larger than our sun. If they continue to expand, they become red supergiants, with a diameter 500 times greater than the sun's.

GIBBERELLINS (jĭb′ə rĕl′ĭnz) Gibberellins are hormones that stimulate plant growth (see HORMONE). They are present in fairly large amounts in seeds, roots, growing stems, and young leaves. Artificial gibberellins have been used to make plants produce flowers or to make germination (sprouting) take place more quickly.

Gibberellins are present in most plants and also in some fungi. Dwarf plants are thought to be deficient in these chemicals.

GIBBON The gibbons are the smallest of the apes. There are six species, belonging to the family Hylobatidae and all living in Southeast Asia. Gibbons vary in color from light brown to black. They are about 3 ft. [90 cm] tall and weigh about 15.4 lb. [7 kg].

Gibbons usually live in small family groups in the tops of trees. Each family establishes a distinct territory. Other families are warned to keep out by the gibbons' loud chattering and howling (see DOMINANCE). Gibbons do not make nests or homes but sleep on branches in the trees. Gibbons use their long arms to swing from branch to branch, sometimes leaping more than 33 ft. [10 m] through the air. They eat young leaves, fruits, insects, birds, and birds' eggs. They leave the trees when they need water. A gibbon drinks by putting its arms in the water and then licking the water off its fur. When walking, gibbons stand upright. They either wave their arms in the air or wrap them around their necks for balance. Gibbons are among the few animals that are afraid of the water and cannot swim.

The siamang is the largest of the gibbons. It is black with a white band on its belly. Its index and middle fingers are connected by a weblike flap of skin. The siamang has an air pouch in its throat, which it uses to produce loud screams.

GILA MONSTER A Gila monster is a large, poisonous lizard that belongs to the family Helodermatidae. It is one of only two species of poisonous lizards in the world. The Gila monster is found in the southwestern United States and in Mexico. It grows to 24 in. [60 cm] in length and may weigh as much as 6 1/2 lb. [3 kg]. The lizard has black, pink, and yellow scales over its short body. Gila monsters eat birds' eggs and all kinds of small animals. Despite its poison, it is rarely dangerous to humans because it must chew on its prey for some time in order to inject its poison.
See also LIZARD.

GILA MONSTER
The Gila monster is one of only two kinds of poisonous lizards. It is named for the Gila River in Arizona.

GILBERT, WILLIAM (1544–1603) William Gilbert was an English physician. He was born in Colchester and studied at Cambridge University. He became physician to Queen Elizabeth I in 1601.

His most important work was not in medicine. Gilbert is famous for his discoveries about magnetism. He discovered that the earth behaves like a magnet. He showed that a compass needle points to the earth's magnetic poles. Gilbert was the first to discover that a magnetic needle also dips toward the earth. The French scientist Peter Peregrinus thought this was because one end of the needle was attracted to heaven. Gilbert showed that, in fact, it was because the other end was attracted to the earth (see MAGNETISM).

GIBBON
Gibbons are agile climbers and the smallest members of the ape family. They live in small family groups in the tops of trees in Southeast Asia.

Gilbert also examined the attraction between amber and small pieces of matter. He coined the word *electricity* from the Greek word for amber, *elektron* (see ELECTRICITY). Gilbert was not always right, however. He believed that the moon was held in orbit around the earth by magnetism. It was about sixty years later that Sir Isaac Newton proved that it was not magnetism but gravitation that did this (see NEWTON, SIR ISAAC). The gilbert, a unit of magnetomotive force, is named for Gilbert.

GILBRETH FAMILY

Gilbreth is the family name of two pioneers in industrial engineering. Frank Bunker Gilbreth and Lillian Evelyn Moller Gilbreth were the first to apply modern ideas about psychology and efficiency to the workplace. The Gilbreths improved the study of time and motion. Such study analyzes how workers perform certain tasks to determine if they are wasting time or energy. The Gilbreths invented many procedures that saved time in factories while keeping the workers from getting too tired. Together, they wrote *Fatigue Study, Applied Motion Study,* and *Motion Study for the Handicapped.* The Gilbreths applied many of their efficiency techniques to raising their twelve children. Two of their children wrote about their family in two books, *Cheaper by the Dozen,* which was made into a motion picture in the 1950s, and *Belles on Their Toes,* filmed in 1952.

Frank Bunker Gilbreth

(1868–1924) Frank Gilbreth was born in Fairfield, Maine. He began building a successful contracting firm in 1895. He married Lillian in 1904. They formed a consulting firm in 1911 and advised many of the top corporations in the United States about worker efficiency. Frank Gilbreth founded several organizations concerned with improving worker conditions and applying science and efficiency to management.

Lillian Evelyn Moller Gilbreth

(1878–1972) Lillian Gilbreth was born in Oakland, California. She attended the University of California at Berkeley. She was graduated with a master's degree in literature. Later, she attended Columbia University in New York City and Brown University in Rhode Island. Gilbreth received a doctoral degree in industrial psychology from Brown University.

GILLS

Gills are organs found in fish and many other water-dwelling animals. The animals use gills to breathe (see BREATHING). Gills take oxygen out of the water, just like humans' lungs take oxygen out of the air (see LUNG). If there is no oxygen in the water, the gills cannot work, and the animal will suffocate. This is the reason that an aquarium with fish in it must have air bubbled through it.

Gills are made up of many fine, threadlike pieces called filaments and they are usually well supplied with blood. In fish, the gills are found in the throat and head area. A fresh supply of water enters the fish's mouth and passes over the gills, which absorb oxygen from the water and release carbon dioxide from the blood. The water flows out of the fish's body through the gill openings on the sides of the body. Most fish are able to pump fresh supplies of

GILLS

The gill cover has been removed from this dead pike (above) to show the gills beneath. The gills of the damselfly larva (below) are the feathery structures at the end of its body.

water over their gills by opening and closing their mouths and contracting their muscles. Some species of sharks are unable to do this. They must continually swim with their mouths open to make sure fresh supplies of water pass over their gills.

Crustaceans, mollusks, the larvae of amphibians, some water insects, and some other animals also have gills. These gills may look different from those of fish and may be located in a different place, but they work in the same basic way.

GINGER FAMILY The ginger family includes about seven hundred species of monocotyledonous tropical plants (see MONOCOTYLEDON). Ginger itself, from tropical Asia, produces slender stems and narrow, grasslike leaves from root-bearing rhizomes (see RHIZOME). The flowers grow in clusters and have yellowish green petals with purple streaks. The rhizomes are dug up when the plants are 9–12 months old, and dried to produce black ginger. To produce white ginger, they are scraped, cleaned, and dried. Ginger is used as a spice in main dishes, cookies, candies, cakes, and beverages such as ginger ale, ginger beer, and ginger wine. Oil of ginger is used to help relieve toothaches and stomachaches.

Wild ginger is a North American plant belonging to the birthwort family. Although not related to the ginger family, its roots produce a gingerlike spice. Wild ginger is a small plant with heart-shaped leaves and small, bell-shaped purple flowers.

GINGER FAMILY

The rhizomes (underground stems) of the ginger plant are dried and powdered to make ginger for flavoring foods and drinks. Or, the fresh rhizomes may be peeled and preserved in syrup. Ginger is then eaten as a candy or dessert.

GINKGO (gĭng´ kō) The ginkgo is a primitive tree that is also called the maidenhair tree. It has unusual fan-shaped leaves and a small egg-shaped fruit. The ginkgo is a popular ornamental tree that was first imported from China and Japan.

GINKGO

The leaves of the primitive ginkgo tree turn yellow in the fall.

GINSENG FAMILY The ginseng family includes about six hundred species of dicotyledonous temperate and tropical plants (see DICOTYLEDON). The two herbs commonly called "ginseng" belong to the genus *Panax,* meaning "panacea," or cure-all (see HERB). In fact, the Chinese species has been used as a medicine for centuries. The roots are used to produce a substance that is believed to have many helpful properties. The word *ginseng* comes from Chinese words meaning "likeness of a man" and refers to the shape of the plant's roots. The other major species is grown in North America. Both are small, perennial herbs with five-lobed leaves. The flowers are small and usually yellowish green in color. Another genus in this family includes the English ivy. This is a climbing plant with shiny evergreen leaves. The leaves are leathery to the touch. The plant is found wild throughout Europe and has been introduced to North America.

GIRAFFE The giraffe is the tallest animal in the world. The bulls (males) grow to a height of 18 ft. [5.5 m] and may weigh more than 2,200 lb. [1,000 kg]. These hoofed mammals live in the African savannas, which are the lightly wooded grasslands south of the Sahara desert (see MAMMAL). Their bodies are yellowish brown with large, dark brown patches. Their coloring provides good camouflage among the trees (see CAMOUFLAGE). The giraffe has a bony bump between its eyes. It has two bony horns on its head covered with skin and hair. The giraffe also has muscles with which it can close its nostrils to keep out sand and dust. The giraffe can extend its tongue as far as 20 in. [50 cm]. It uses this tongue and its large lips to pick leaves from trees. This herbivore, or plant eater, is a ruminant and chews its food two separate times before digesting it (see RUMINANT). In order to drink, the giraffe spreads its front legs and lowers its head down to the water.

The giraffe's long neck has seven vertebrae, the same number that most mammals have (see VERTEBRA). Its neck has a short mane that extends from the head to the back. The giraffe's tail is about 3 ft. [90 cm] long and ends in a long tuft of hair.

Giraffes travel in herds of twenty to thirty. A cow (female giraffe) first mates when she is four or five years old. After a pregnancy of about fifteen months, she gives birth to a single calf. This calf may be as tall as 6 ft. [1.8 m] and may weigh about 150 lb. [68 kg]. The calf nurses for almost a year. Most giraffes live to be fifteen to twenty years old.

Aside from human beings, the lion is the only major natural enemy of giraffes, though leopards may attack the young. However, because a giraffe's hooves are such deadly weapons, even a lion rarely attacks an adult giraffe. A giraffe can run at a speed of 30 m.p.h. [48 kph] for an extended period of time without tiring. A healthy giraffe rarely lies down. It even sleeps standing up.

GLACIATION Glaciation is the process by which huge masses of ice, called glaciers, form from snow (see GLACIER). The ice then erodes, or wears down, the landscape. Glaciers have had a tremendous influence on the landscape of northern areas of the earth. During the Pleistocene epoch, which

GIRAFFE
A giraffe family—bull, cow, and calf—walks across the savanna in central Africa. The trees in the background are acacias, a favorite food of giraffes.

began 1.64 million years ago and ended about 10,000 years ago, large parts of North America, Europe, and Asia were glaciated or shaped by glaciers.

The movement of glaciers shapes the land by wearing away rocks. Glaciers also pick up and deposit rocks elsewhere. When a glacier flows across cracked rocks, it may lift up huge stones. This process is called quarrying. Ice freezes around quarried rocks and embeds them at the bottom of the glacier, forming "teeth." As the glacier moves, these teeth scratch other rocks. These scratches are called striations. Scientists can determine the direction of ice movements by studying striations.

Around the upper part of a glacier, steep-sided basins called cirques form. Often, several cirques form and are separated by ridges called arêtes. The peaks that occur where several cirques come together are called horns. An example of a horn is the Matterhorn in Switzerland.

Valleys formed by glaciers are usually steep-sided and U-shaped. They often have waterfalls. The famous fjords of Norway formed in glacial valleys (see FJORD).

Rocks and soil moved by glaciers are called moraines. This debris may form a ridge, called a terminal moraine, at the outermost limit of a melting glacier. As the glacier retreats, it deposits recessional moraines. These are ridges that mark where the glacier stopped temporarily during its retreat (see MORAINE).

Fine material carried by glaciers is deposited as boulder clay. It sometimes forms low hills called drumlins. Drumlins are particularly evident in New England. Sometimes, a stone or boulder is deposited by a glacier in an area of different geological composition. These stones or boulders are called erratics. Eskers are low, winding ridges that form where glacial streams once flowed beneath the ice.
See also GEOMORPHOLOGY; ICE AGE.

GLACIATION

The results of glaciation can clearly be seen in this steep-sided valley in Norway. The slow-moving ice of a glacier scoured away the rocks, leaving them exposed after the ice melted.

GLACIER Glaciers are huge, slow-moving masses of snow and ice that occur on land. Glaciers today cover about 10 percent of the earth's land surface. During the last ice age, however, they covered as much as 30 percent (see ICE AGE). There are two main types of glaciers—continental glaciers and valley glaciers.

Continental glaciers, or ice sheets, cover large areas of land. Ice sheets cover almost all of Antarctica and about 85 percent of Greenland. These huge ice sheets bury the entire area, so that only the tallest mountains are still visible. Continental glaciers build from the middle and spread out in all directions. The Antarctic ice sheet is almost 6,500 ft. [2,000 m] deep in some places. Other continental glaciers are found in northern Canada, Iceland, and Norway.

Valley glaciers occur on all the continents. They form on mountains above the permanent snow line. This is the point where the annual snowfall is greater than the loss of snow by melting. The permanent snow line is at a high altitude near the equator. It is close to sea level in some polar regions. Valley glaciers start to form when the snowfall is greater than the snow melt. The snow then becomes compacted into ice crystals called névé. Water seeps into the névé and freezes. Gradually, the white névé becomes a clear, glacial blue.

When the ice becomes thick enough, it begins to move downhill because of gravity and its own weight. The friction between the earth and the glacier causes the bottom ice to melt and refreeze, thus helping the glacier move more easily. A dangerous feature of glaciers is the crevasses, or cracks, that occur in the ice. Crevasses may be very deep and are often hidden by loose snow. They form because the upper levels of the glacier are moving faster than the lower levels.

Valley glaciers move rather slowly, usually just a few feet a day. The fastest recorded advance of a glacier occurred in Alaska, when the Black Rapids Glacier moved as fast as 200 ft. [61 m] a day. The increased speed was caused by an earthquake.

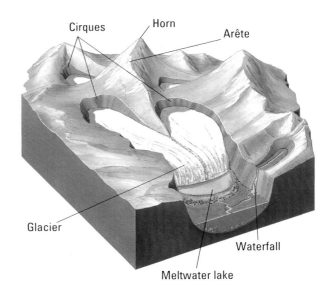

GLACIER—Erosion
The moving ice has a scouring action on the rocks around it, forming arêtes (ridges), hollows (cirques), and deep valleys (above). Meltwater from beneath the ice may form a small lake at the foot of the glacier.

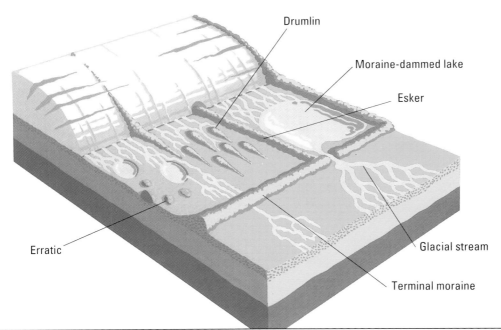

GLACIER—Deposition
As the ice of a glacier melts and the foot of the glacier retreats, rocks and rubble that the glacier pushed along become exposed. The various types of formation are shown in the diagram (left).

GLACIER—Lake

Continental glaciers move even more slowly, just a few feet each year. Where a continental glacier meets the ocean, sections of it break off to form icebergs. These usually float to warmer waters and eventually melt. Icebergs that are hundreds of miles wide have been sighted.

GLADIOLUS *Gladiolus* is a genus of about three hundred species of perennial flowering plants belonging to the iris family. They are native to Africa, Asia, and southern Europe, but are now

GLADIOLUS
Gladioli (plural of *gladiolus*) are popular garden flowers that grow from underground stems called corms.

grown all over the world. Gladioli (plural of *gladiolus*) grow from underground stems called corms (see BULB AND CORM). Tube-shaped flowers grow along one side of the spike, a stem that grows as tall as 3 ft. [90 cm]. The name *gladiolus* means "little sword." It refers to this spike and the sword-shaped leaves. The flowers have various colors, depending on the species. These popular garden plants are sometimes called sword lilies.
See also IRIS FAMILY.

GLAND A gland is a structure in a human being or other animal that produces and releases special fluids or scents. There are two kinds of glands. One type, called an exocrine gland, releases its secretions through tiny tubes, called ducts. The secretions may leave the body or pass to a particular part of the body to do a specific job. Exocrine glands exist in the skin for producing sweat. Exocrine glands also produce the saliva that flows into the mouth. Other exocrine glands are the tear glands of the eye, the milk-producing glands in a woman's breasts, and the mucus glands found in the nose, mouth, and other passageways that open to the outside of the body. All of these glands release their products to the outside of the body. Other exocrine glands are located in the walls of the stomach and intestines. They release their chemicals (the juices that digest food) into the digestive tract. The liver and a part of the pancreas are also glands that produce digestive juices.

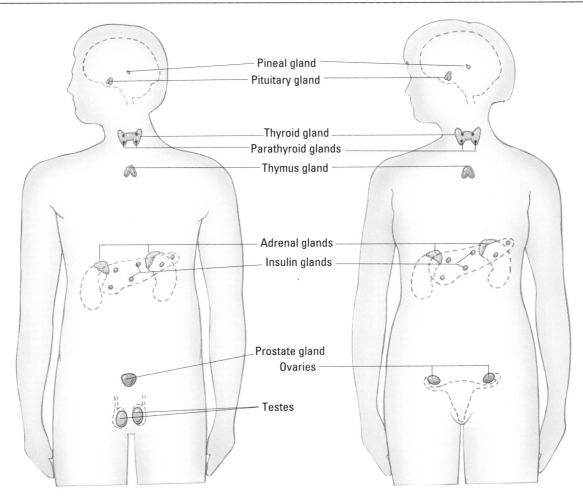

Pineal gland
Pituitary gland

Thyroid gland
Parathyroid glands
Thymus gland

Adrenal glands
Insulin glands

Prostate gland
Ovaries

Testes

The second kind of gland does not have a duct. These glands are called ductless or endocrine glands. They release chemicals into the bloodstream. The chemicals made by ductless glands are called hormones. Hormones are carried in the blood to various organs of the body. They make these organs work in a particular way (see ENDOCRINE; HORMONE). The glands may release their hormones in response to "messages" from part of the nervous system. Many other factors, including hormones from other endocrine glands, may also participate in a gland's control.

The pancreas produces a hormone called insulin. Insulin controls the amount of sugar in the blood. With insulin present, sugar in the blood is taken up by cells and used as fuel for cellular processes. If something goes wrong with the pancreas, not enough insulin may be produced. Consequently, there will be too much sugar in the blood. This may cause the disease known as diabetes mellitus.

See also DIABETES; INSULIN.

GLAND—Male and female

Males and females have the same glands except for those having to do with reproduction. A male (left) has testes and a prostate gland, whereas a female (right) has ovaries. All are endocrine glands that produce hormones, except for the prostate gland in males, which is an exocrine gland.

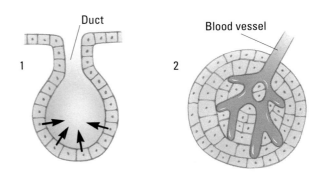

Duct

Blood vessel

1

2

GLAND—Exocrine and endocrine

(1) Exocrine glands such as salivary glands and sweat glands have ducts for releasing their products into body cavities or onto the skin. (2) Endocrine glands have no ducts and release their products—hormones—directly into the bloodstream.

GLASS

Glass is a hard substance usually made of sand and various chemicals. Most glass is transparent. However, it can be colored to any shade. It has an almost countless number of uses. Food is kept in glass jars. People drink from containers called glasses. Windows in nearly every building are made of glass. Automobiles have glass windshields and windows. Glass is used in thermometers and in lenses for microscopes, telescopes, and many other instruments. Besides being functional, glass is often used for decoration. Many works of art are made of glass.

Glass is usually made from such common substances as sand, soda, and lime. It has many properties. It is easy to shape. It can be spun finer than a human hair. It can also be molded into a disk weighing many tons. Glass can be stronger than steel or more fragile than paper. Glass is resistant to all kinds of weather and to most chemicals. It is also a good electrical insulator in that it prevents the flow of electricity (see INSULATION).

Glass appears to be a solid. It has many properties of a solid. Glass, however, is really a very thick liquid. It is a supercooled liquid. This means that it was cooled below its freezing point before it became a solid (see SUPERCOOLING). Most common glasses are amorphous. In other words, their atoms are not arranged in a regular, repeating order, as atoms are in a crystal.

Types of glass Soda-lime glasses make up about 90 percent of all glasses manufactured. They are made up of three basic ingredients. One is sand, chemically known as silicon dioxide (SiO_2). Another is lime, which is calcium carbonate ($CaCO_3$). The third is sodium carbonate (Na_2CO_3). These substances make glasses that are easy to melt and shape.

Lead glasses are made with lead monoxide (PbO) instead of lime. Lead monoxide is mixed with sand, sodium carbonate, and small amounts of other materials. Lead glasses are used for objects such as lenses, art objects, and tableware. Lead glasses are also good electrical insulators. They are used to make such items as tubing for neon lighting.

Borosilicate glasses are made of silicon dioxide, boric oxide (B_2O_3), and aluminum oxide (Al_2O_3). This type of glass resists heat, shock, and chemical damage and is also a good electrical insulator. The most familiar forms of this glass are known best by the trade name Pyrex. These are used in kitchen ovenware, laboratory equipment, and industrial piping.

MAKING GLASS

The four chief ingredients in making glass are soda ash (sodium carbonate), limestone (calcium carbonate), sand (silicon dioxide), and cullet (recycled waste glass). The ingredients are melted in a furnace. The glass from the furnace may be allowed to cool as sheets for glazing, or shaped in molds to make articles such as bottles.

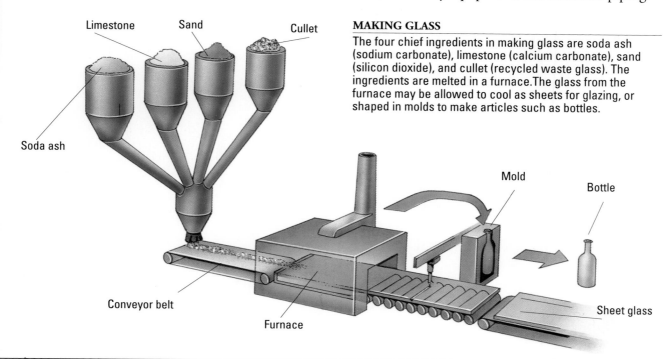

Limestone Sand Cullet

Soda ash

Mold

Bottle

Conveyor belt

Furnace

Sheet glass

Silica glasses are made with the same ingredients as borosilicate glass. The mixture, however, is first treated with acid. A porous substance is left. It is heated to a high temperature, and the glass shrinks. The pores close, and a transparent, nonporous glass is the end product. Silica glasses can undergo tremendous changes in temperatures. They can be taken out of a red-hot oven and placed in ice-cold water without breaking. Silica glasses are used for ovenware, appliance parts, and antenna shields in space vehicles. Fused silica glass is made from silica alone. It can be formed into many shapes and sizes. It is used in electronics equipment.

Colored glass is made by adding small amounts of metal oxides (compounds of metal and oxygen) to clear glass. Compounds of copper and cobalt help make glass blue. Chromium compounds give glass a green color.

Photosensitive glasses are those in which images from photographic negatives can be reproduced. The image is produced after the glasses are exposed to ultraviolet rays. The glasses are then treated by heat, chemicals, or other treatments. Electrical-

SILICA GLASS

Glass made from melted silica is heat resistant. It is used to make windows for spacecraft as well as mirrors for high-energy lasers.

conducting glasses are made by fusing a metallic oxide coating to the surface of borosilicate glasses. These glasses are used in panels for heating.

Fibrous glasses are tiny threads of glass that have been twisted or compressed together. The threads are made by forcing molten glass through tiny dies, or molds. This material is used in air filters and textiles, as a binder for some plastics, and in optical fibers.

Cellular glasses are made by heating crushed glass with materials that produce gases at certain temperatures. The melting glass foams. When it cools, the foam becomes rigid. These glasses are lightweight. They float in water. They can be drilled, sawed, and shaped without shattering or chipping. They are excellent heat insulators. They are used in many of the same ways as fibrous glasses.

Glass ceramic objects are first fashioned from a special glass containing certain materials called nucleating agents. When heated, these agents cause numerous small crystals to form. The product is opaque (nontransparent). It shows high strength, greater hardness, and more impact resistance than ordinary glass (see CERAMICS).

ORNAMENTAL GLASS

Metallic compounds can be added to glass during manufacture to give it color. These glasses were colored blue by adding a compound of cobalt.

How glass is made A glass factory looks different from most kinds of factories. Huge bins, called silos, hold the raw materials for glassmaking. These materials are all dry powders. They appear to be similar, but they can produce many different results. Giant ventilators and huge smokestacks release the tremendous heat that is needed to melt these powders into a liquid.

After the main raw materials are carefully weighed and mixed in the proper quantities, the glassmaker adds cullet. Cullet is recycled glass or waste glass from a previous melting. Adding cullet to the new batch of glass uses materials that otherwise would be wasted. The addition of cullet can also reduce the amount of heat needed to melt the new batch.

In early times, the batch was melted in small clay pots called refractory pots that were usually heated by wood fires. Special modern refractory pots hold up to 3,000 lb. [1,400 kg] of glass. They are heated by gas or oil. A single furnace may hold up to twenty pots.

Larger amounts of glass are made in furnaces called day tanks. Day tanks can hold 1 to 4 tons [0.9 to 3.6 metric tons] of glass. Most glass is melted in larger furnaces called continuous tanks. The largest continuous tanks can melt 400 to 600 tons [360 to 540 metric tons] a day.

How glass is shaped and finished There are four main ways of shaping glass: blowing, pressing, drawing, and casting. Blowing glass without the use of molds is an art that is about two thousand years old. A hollow iron blowpipe is dipped into the molten glass. Some of the molten glass sticks to the pear-shaped end of the blowpipe. A person blows softly into the pipe. The glass bulges out and forms a hollow bulb. The glass can be squeezed, stretched, and cut. When the red-hot glass has been given its final shape, it is removed from the pipe. Glass can also be blown in iron molds, by hand or by machine.

Pressing is performed by dropping a large, hot drop of glass in a mold. The liquid glass is then pressed until it spreads and fills the inside of the mold. Baking dishes, glass blocks, and lenses

GLASS IN BUILDING
Modern buildings make extensive use of glass. These skyscrapers are in Tampa, Florida.

are often pressed. Pressing can be done by hand or by machine.

A technique called drawing is used to shape flat glass, glass tubing, and fiberglass. Flat glass is shaped by drawing a wide sheet of molten glass into a tank of molten tin. This tank is called a float bath. The glass floats in an even layer on the smooth surface of the molten tin. Because glass turns solid at a higher temperature than tin, the glass can be moved from the molten tin for further cooling. Glass tubing is made by drawing a stream of molten glass around a rotating cylinder or cone called a mandrel. Air blowing through the mandrel causes the glass to form a continuous tube. Fiberglass is made by drawing molten glass through tiny holes in the bottom of the furnace (see FIBERGLASS).

Casting is a technique that involves filling molds with molten glass. Casting is used in the production of huge disks, such as the 200-in. [508-cm] mirror for the telescope of the Palomar Observatory in California.

Lampworking is used to reshape glass into new forms after it has cooled. Lampworkers reheat many kinds of glass tubing over a blowtorch fired by gas and oxygen. Then they can bend, twist, stretch, and seal the softened glass into a variety of objects.

Annealing is a way of removing the stresses and strains remaining in glass objects after shaping. Annealing is done by reheating the glass and gradually cooling it according to a planned time and temperature schedule (see ANNEALING).

Tempering is a method in which a glass object that is already formed is reheated until it is almost soft. Then, under carefully controlled conditions, the glass is chilled suddenly by blasts of cold air. It may also be chilled by oil or certain chemicals in a liquid state. Tempering makes the glass much stronger than ordinary glass.

There are numerous ways of decorating glass objects. Hydrofluoric acid and some of its compounds are the only chemicals that easily dissolve glass. Glass articles dipped in or sprayed by these chemicals are said to be etched. Depending on the makeup of the glass, the strength of the etching compound, and time, an etched-glass surface may be rough, frosted, and almost opaque. On the other hand, it may have a translucent, soft, silky appearance. Sandblasting also gives a translucent surface, though usually rougher than that obtained by etching. In sandblasting, compressed air blows coarse, rough-grained sand against the glass, often through a rubber stencil, to form a design.

Cutting is a way of wearing away large amounts of glass by holding it against revolving sandstone or carborundum wheels.

Copper-wheel engraving allows very fine details. Major masterpieces of art are engraved this way. The process involves the painstaking cutting of glass with dozens of abrasive-fed copper wheels. Coloring materials also can be applied to glass. When these materials are heated to the proper temperature, they fuse to the glass, becoming part of the article. Tumblers, jugs, pitchers, and many other glass products are decorated this way.

STAINED GLASS

Window glass can be colored or painted to make pictures. This stained-glass window is in an old manor house in England.

GLAUCOMA

GLAUCOMA (glou kō′mə) Glaucoma is a disease of the eye. It is caused by an increase in the amount of fluid inside the eyeball (see EYE AND VISION). The fluid presses against the retina and the other delicate internal parts of the eye, damaging them. Damage to the retina causes a decrease in vision. Glaucoma usually occurs over many years. Often, patients will not be aware of any symptoms at all. This is why regular visits to the ophthalmologist (eye doctor) are important. Sometimes, glaucoma can come on suddenly. When this happens, a person may have a sore, red eye and see colored halos around lamps and other lights.

Glaucoma is usually treated by medication, though surgery is sometimes done. The surgeon makes a cut in the eyeball so that the fluid can drain away. If glaucoma is not treated, blindness can occur.

GLENN, JOHN HERSCHEL (1921–)

John Glenn was the first American to orbit the earth. On February 20, 1962, he went around the earth three times in the spacecraft *Friendship 7*. The flight lasted 4 hours and 56 minutes. It flew 160 mi. [258 km] above the earth's surface. Glenn was the third man to make the journey in space around the earth. The first was Yuri Gagarin, of the former Soviet Union, in April 1961 (see GAGARIN, YURI ALEKSEYEVICH). He made one orbit around the earth. The second was also a Soviet, Gherman Titov. He made sixteen orbits in August 1961.

John Glenn was born in Cambridge, Ohio. He was a fighter pilot and trained as a test pilot before becoming an astronaut. He was one of the first

JOHN GLENN
John Glenn was the first American astronaut to orbit the earth. His three-orbit, five-hour trip was made in the spacecraft *Friendship 7* in February 1962.

seven American astronauts. Two of the others were Alan Shepherd and Virgil I. Grissom. They made spaceflights the year before Glenn but did not orbit the earth.

John Glenn left the space program in 1964 to pursue a career in politics. After two unsuccessful attempts, he was elected to the U.S. Senate from Ohio in 1974. In 1983, Glenn campaigned to become the Democratic party's candidate for president. However, he later withdrew because he lacked support. In 1987, Glenn became the chairman of the U.S. Senate government affairs committee. In 1976, Glenn was inducted into the Aviation Hall of Fame.

GLUCOSE

GLUCOSE Glucose ($C_6H_{12}O_6$), a white crystalline sugar, is in the class of foods or nutrients called carbohydrates (see CARBOHYDRATE; CRYSTAL; SUGAR). Glucose is one of the group of sugars called hexoses. Each molecule of glucose is based on a ring of six atoms—five carbon atoms and an oxygen atom. There are two forms of glucose—α-D-glucose, or dextrose, and ß-D-glucose. These forms are called anomers. They are chemically identical, but only dextrose occurs in living organisms.

Glucose is described by scientists as being a monosaccharide, or single sugar, which means it is a sugar with a simple structure. Glucose is made by plants during photosynthesis (see PHOTOSYNTHESIS). Most commonly, it is then converted to starch and stored. Starch is a *polysaccharide,* a term that means "many sugars." Glucose is also a part of disaccharides, which are made up of two sugars. Common disaccharides are lactose, which is the sugar in milk, and sucrose, which is regular table sugar.

During digestion, carbohydrates in food are broken down to glucose (see DIGESTION). After a meal rich in carbohydrates, some of the extra glucose is stored in the liver and muscles as glycogen. Glycogen is built up from molecules of glucose. Some glucose may also be changed to fat. When energy is needed, the stored glycogen can be changed back into glucose. The blood normally contains about 0.1 percent glucose. The amount of glucose in the blood increases in those who have the disease diabetes mellitus. This increase in the amount of glucose in the blood is called hyperglycemia (see DIABETES).

Glucose is commercially made from starch (see STARCH). Starch is mixed with acid and heated under steam pressure. If the change is complete, the glucose is a pure powder. It is sold under the name dextrose. If the change is not complete and the mixture contains glucose with other sugars, the product is called glucose syrup, starch syrup, or corn syrup. Both forms of glucose are widely used in making foods and beverages such as candy and soft drinks.

GLUTEN Gluten is a rather sticky, or glutinous, material found in wheat grains and the flours that are made from them. Its stickiness makes wheat flour particularly good for making bread. The various strains of wheat contain different amounts of gluten. The so-called hard wheats yield strong flours containing between 10 and 14 percent of gluten. These produce a very elastic dough when mixed with water and kneaded well. Soft flours, containing 7 to 10 percent of gluten, yield a more crumbly dough. Flours with less than 7 percent of gluten are not suitable for breadmaking, although they can be used for cakes and cookies. Gluten also occurs in rye grains, although in smaller quantities than it does in wheat. Gluten consists mainly of two proteins, called glutenin and gliadin. Some people are allergic to gliadin and experience severe digestive troubles if they eat it. This is called celiac disease, and people with it must eat a gluten-free diet or at least one with very little gluten in it. Some people with celiac disease can replace wheat flour with rye flour because rye flour has far less gluten.

GLUTEUS MAXIMUS The gluteus maximus is the biggest and most powerful muscle in the human body. It is one of three muscles that make up each of the buttocks. The gluteus maximus is attached at one end to the pelvis and at the other to the thigh bone. Imagine you are bending down to touch your toes. As the gluteus maximus contracts, or gets shorter, it helps pull your body upright again. It also helps you walk upstairs and rise from a sitting position.

GNU The gnu, also called the wildebeest, is a large African antelope that belongs to the family Bovidae (see ANTELOPE). There are two species of gnu in the world. The brindled gnu is common on the East African plains. The white-tailed gnu is now almost extinct. It is found only in a few wildlife reserves in southern Africa (see EXTINCTION). A gnu has a horselike body and a large head with two curved horns.

GNU

The male brindled gnu lowers his ears when approaching a possible mate. The gnu travels hundreds of miles on its yearly migration across the African plains.

GOAT The goat is any of the wild or domestic hoofed mammals belonging to genus *Capra* of the family Bovidae. Other members of the family Bovidae include sheep, cattle, and antelopes. Goats are herbivores and ruminants (see HERBIVORE; RUMINANT). Their hollow horns grow straight back from the head and usually curve near the tip.

Most goats have beards under their chins. The billy goat or buck (male) gives off a strong, foul odor. The nanny goat or doe (female) has a pregnancy of about five months before giving birth to her young, called kids. Wild goats usually give birth to one kid each year. Domestic goats often give birth to two or three kids each year. Most goats live ten to fourteen years. They are able to survive on very sparse vegetation in dry, rocky areas. Most goats are good climbers. They have no trouble moving about among rocks.

Wild goats live in mountainous and rocky areas of Europe, Asia, and northern Africa. The ibex and markhor are wild goats. The Alpine ibex (*Capra ibex*) may weigh as much as 165 lb. [75 kg].

Domestic goats, of which there are many breeds, are descended from the Pasang (*Capra hircus*), a wild goat native to Asia. Domestic goats are usually raised for their milk. They are often called the "poor man's cow." Goats produce a milk that is sweeter and more easily digested than cow's milk. It also has a higher percentage of fat and protein. Goat's milk can be processed into high-quality cheese and butter. Goat hide is used for leather products. Some goat breeds produce valuable wool called mohair or angora.

The Rocky Mountain goat (*Oreamnos americanus*) is not a true goat. It is a goat-antelope like the chamois. It lives in the Rocky Mountains of the United States and Canada.

GOAT

Most goats (top), which belong to the same family as sheep and antelopes, have beards under their chins. Domestic goats, such as these in Kenya (above), are raised for their milk and meat. Their hides are also used to make a durable leather.

GODDARD, ROBERT HUTCHINGS

(1882–1945) Robert Goddard was an American scientist. He was born in Worcester, Massachusetts. He designed rockets for the U.S. Army. His first rockets used solid fuels, but he was not satisfied with these. The Smithsonian Institution gave him a grant to research liquid fuels. Goddard designed the first successful rocket that used liquid fuel (see FUEL). It was launched on March 16, 1926. The power came from combining gasoline and liquid oxygen. Goddard continued making progress on the project. The first rocket traveled at 65 m.p.h. [105 kph]. It climbed to a height of 185 ft. [56 m]. In 1935, Goddard made a rocket that could fly at 700 m.p.h. [1,100 kph]. It climbed as high as 1.5 mi. [2.5 km].

Most of Goddard's work was intended for military use. He died at the end of World War II. His work has been very important in developing space flight. He published a book on space flight called *A Method of Reaching Extreme Altitudes*.

GOLD Gold is a shiny, yellow, metallic element (see ELEMENT). Its chemical symbol is Au (from the Latin name *aurum*).

Gold is a very unreactive metal, meaning that it does not easily form compounds (see COMPOUND). Because of this, it does not tarnish in the air or in water. It keeps its attractive shiny appearance. This has made it very desirable for use in jewelry and ornaments. Gold has been considered very valuable since ancient times because it is rare. Coins have been made of gold for more than two thousand years.

Gold is no longer used in everyday coinage. Special coins and medals are, however, made from it. Gold is used as a standard of currency for trade in various countries. Most of the world's gold is stored in the form of heavy, brick-shaped blocks called ingots. They are kept in heavily guarded bank vaults. Millions of dollars' worth of gold is stored in Fort Knox, Kentucky.

Gold is used for things other than banking and jewelry. It can easily be beaten into different shapes. This makes it useful in dentistry. Fillings and crowns can be molded from it. They do not corrode (see CORROSION). The metal can also be beaten into very thin sheets. Gold leaf may be as thin as ten thousandths of a millimeter. It is used for gilding (covering with gold) and for gold lettering. Gold is a very good conductor of electricity. It is used to make small components in delicate

electrical circuits. Ruby glass contains particles of colloidal gold (see COLLOID).

Gold is often mixed with other metals to form what are called alloys. These mixes are cheaper, but just as attractive. White gold is an alloy of gold with platinum, palladium, nickel, and zinc. Green gold contains gold and silver. Red gold contains gold and copper.

The proportion of gold in an alloy is measured in carats. (This is not the same carat that is used to weigh diamonds.) Pure gold is called 24-carat gold. If an alloy is 14-carat gold, it means that 14 parts out of 24 are gold. The rest is other metals. Very pure gold is too soft for ordinary use. That is why alloys are usually used in jewelry.

Gold is found throughout the world. The main countries mining gold are South Africa, Australia, Russia, the United States, and Canada. The gold is found as lumps, called nuggets, in rocks. It also occurs as fine grains in sand and gravel and as streaks or veins in quartz.

When grains of gold are found in gravel, they may be separated by washing. The heavy grains sink to the bottom as the lighter gravel is washed away. In the past, prospectors used to "pan" for gold. They used shallow pans to wash the gravel from riverbeds. Today, the rock containing the gold is crushed by machinery. It is then treated with

GOLD

The Gold Reef City Mine (above) is near Johannesburg, the center of South Africa's gold-mining industry. The Golden Temple at Amritsar, India (right), is so-called because it is covered with gold leaf. Gold is found buried in the ground as nuggets (below), or as particles in stream beds, called alluvial gold.

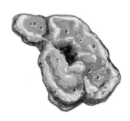

chemicals that dissolve the gold. The gold compounds that are formed are then treated with other chemicals to release the gold. The processes of electrolysis and distillation may also be used to extract the metal (see DISTILLATION; ELECTROLYSIS).

Gold is not attacked by most acids. However, one acid that will dissolve it is called aqua regia. This is a mixture of concentrated hydrochloric acid and concentrated nitric acid.

Gold's atomic number is 79. Its relative atomic mass is 196.97. Gold melts at 1,945°F [1,063°C]. It boils at 4,820°F [2,660°C]. It is one of the densest metals, but it is a little lighter than platinum. *See also* RELATIVE DENSITY.

GOLDENROD

Goldenrod is the name of about one hundred species of wildflowers belonging to the genus *Solidago* in the composite family (see COMPOSITE FAMILY). These perennial plants are native to North America (see PERENNIAL PLANT). They have alternate, toothed leaves and yellow flowers. The flowers are made up of florets and usually grow in dense clusters (see FLOWER; LEAF).

Goldenrod is often cultivated as an ornamental garden flower. Its leaves can be used to make tea. In some countries, the flowers are processed into a yellow dye. Contrary to popular belief, the pollen of goldenrod does not cause allergies. It is too wet and sticky to be carried more than a short distance by the wind.

GOLDENROD

The yellow flowers of goldenrod form a striking part of the autumn landscape in North America.

GOLDFISH

A goldfish is a freshwater fish that belongs to the carp and minnow family, Cyprinidae. It is a close relative to the carp and sometimes mates with carp. The fish is called a goldfish because its color is generally orangish gold. Like the carp, goldfish originally came from Asia and were spread around the world by people. A common household pet, goldfish now exist in a huge range of shapes and colors. They have been set free so often that they are now found in most major waterways. Although pet goldfish stay quite small, goldfish can grow as long as 10 in. [25.4 cm]. *See also* CARP; MINNOW.

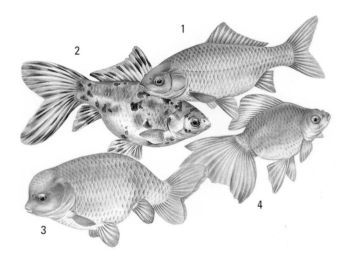

GOLDFISH

Apart from its color, the common goldfish (1) closely resembles the carp from which it was bred. The shubunkin (2), lionhead (3), and veiltail (4) are some of the many types of fancy goldfish that people keep in home aquariums.

GONORRHEA

(gŏn′ə rē′ ə) Gonorrhea is an infectious disease. It is one of the most common sexually transmitted diseases. It is usually spread by sexual intercourse (see DISEASE; INFECTION; SEX). Gonorrhea is caused by a bacterium called *Neisseria gonorrhoeae*. In the male, gonorrhea can cause a puslike, yellowish discharge, or fluid, from the penis. There is often a burning feeling in the penis when urinating. In the female, gonorrhea may cause a puslike discharge from the vagina. In most cases, however, the woman has no symptoms and may not know she has the disease.

Gonorrhea usually appears a few days after

contact with an infected person. The symptoms will disappear in about a week, but the disease continues. If untreated, gonorrhea may cause great damage to the reproductive system. Frequently, the man or woman will become sterile (unable to produce children). A baby born to a mother with gonorrhea may get the disease as it passes through the birth canal. The disease often affects the baby's eyes and may cause blindness. Many states require that all newborn babies be given an antibiotic ointment called erythromycin to prevent the possibility of blindness from gonorrhea.

Gonorrhea can be treated with penicillin. In recent years, however, the disease has developed new strains that are resistant to penicillin and other antibiotics (see ANTIBIOTIC). Any damage caused by the disease is permanent and cannot be reversed. Since gonorrhea is so contagious and affects millions of people each year, it is important that anyone who has sexual contact with an infected person receive treatment as soon as possible.

See also REPRODUCTION; SEXUALLY TRANSMITTED DISEASES.

GOODALL, JANE (1934–) Jane Goodall is a British ethologist, or scientist who studies behavior patterns of animals. She is one of the world's most

famous experts on the behavior of chimpanzees and other primates (see CHIMPANZEE; PRIMATE). Goodall traveled to Africa when she was eighteen and worked with archeologists Louis and Mary Leakey (see LEAKEY FAMILY). In spite of the fact that Goodall had no formal training or college degree at that time, she was soon respected by scientists.

In 1960, Goodall began to study chimpanzees at the Gombe Stream Research Center in Tanzania, Africa. Her method of close daily contact earned the trust of the chimpanzees. This allowed her to observe their individual characteristics. Goodall was the first scientist to make regular observations of chimpanzees in their natural environment. She concentrated on the behavior patterns of individuals, rather than just the behavior patterns of the group. Goodall was the first scientist to report that chimpanzees are not completely vegetarian (plant eating). She found chimpanzees also may hunt, kill, and eat small animals. Goodall also discovered that chimpanzees make simple tools to obtain food and water. Until then, scientists believed human beings were the only animals who made tools.

Goodall also studied other animals in Africa, such as the baboon and hyena. She is now scientific director at Gombe Stream Research Center and is also the director of the Jane Goodall Institute. This

JANE GOODALL

Jane Goodall became famous for her studies of the behavior of chimpanzees in the wild. She made regular observations of individual animals that soon learned to trust her.

organization was set up in the 1970s to promote wildlife research and education, particularly in the sphere of welfare and conservation of wild and captive chimpanzees. The organization has branches in the U.S., Canada, and the U.K. Her books include *My Life with the Chimpanzees* and *In the Shadow of Man.*

GOOGOL A googol is a very large number that is sometimes used by mathematicians. It is 10 multiplied by itself 100 times. In other words, it is 1 followed by 100 zeros. This is written as 10^{100}.

Mathematicians have always been fascinated by large numbers. Such numbers can be related to the immense size of the universe. For example, the number of atoms in the solar system is about 10^{57}, or 1 followed by 57 zeros. The number of atoms in the whole Milky Way galaxy, of which our solar system is a very tiny part, is about 10^{70}. It has been estimated that the number of atoms in the entire universe may be about 10^{80}. This number is still very much smaller than a googol.

Even though the googol seems like an incredibly big number, the googolplex is much bigger still. The googolplex is a 1 followed by a googol of zeros, or $10^{10^{100}}$. Another way to write a googolplex would be $10,000,000,000^{100}$. That is 10 billion multiplied by itself 100 times. The number of atoms in the whole universe is very small compared to a googolplex.

The name *googol,* a child's word, was chosen by the nine-year-old nephew of the American mathematician Edward Kasner (1878–1955).

GOOSE Geese are large water birds that belong to the family Anatidae. They are generally larger than ducks but smaller than swans. There are nine species of geese found in North America. Most species are black, brown, and white. The snow goose and the rare Ross's goose are nearly all white. Perhaps the best-known goose is the Canada goose. It can grow to 25 in. [62.5 cm] in length with a wingspan of 68 in. [170 cm]. This goose makes a familiar honking noise. Domestic geese, which are reared all over the world for meat and eggs, are all descended from the Eurasian greylag goose.

Although geese may feed in the water, they usually graze on grain and grasses on land. Canada geese spend the summer in northern lands of Canada and the United States. In the winter, they fly to the southern and coastal United States and Mexico. Geese migrate long distances in V-shaped flocks.

See also BIRD; MIGRATION.

GOOSE

The pink-footed goose (top), from Asia and Europe, is named for its bright pink legs and feet. The Hawaiian goose (bottom), shown here stomping the ground in a so-called triumph display, has little webbing on its feet. This feature suits it for walking on the rocky lava where it lives.

GOOSEBERRY The gooseberry is one of two species of small, compact shrubs belonging to the currant family (see CURRANT). Gooseberries are native to the cooler temperate regions of North

GOOSEBERRY

Gooseberries taste sour and need plenty of sugar when used for jellies and desserts.

America and Europe. They produce a hairy, oval-shaped fruit that may be red, white, yellow, or green. This bitter fruit is used in jellies, jams, preserves, and pies. The two species are the American gooseberry and the European gooseberry.

GOOSEFOOT FAMILY

The goosefoot family, Chenopodiaceae, includes 100 genera (plural of *genus)* and more than 1,500 species of herbaceous plants, shrubs, and trees. They are dicotyledons and grow well in many parts of the world, including in salt marshes and near oceans (see DICOTYLE-DON; HALOPHYTE; HERBACEOUS PLANT). In general, they have alternate leaves, which may be fleshy or scaly (see LEAF). The stems frequently are covered with white scales. The flowers are usually small and green.

Many important root crops, such as beets and sugar beets, are members of this family. Spinach is also a member of the goosefoot family. This family gets its name from the fact that some species have leaves that resemble the webbed foot of a goose. The goosefoot plant is a tall annual weed native to North America, Europe, and Asia. It ranges in height from 1 ft. [30 cm] to 10 ft. [3 m]. Clusters of tiny green flowers droop from the stem. The fleshy leaves are sometimes cooked and eaten as greens. The goosefoot plant is also called pigweed or lamb's-quarters.

GOPHER

The gopher is any of about thirty species of burrowing rodents (see RODENT). These mammals are native to North America. They may grow as long as 18 in. [45 cm]. Gophers usually live in underground darkness and have poor eyesight. They use their chisel-like front teeth and their sharp claws to dig complex underground tunnels that may be more than 792 ft. [240 m] long. The tail is tactile, which means it has a sense of touch. This is important when the gopher backs its way through a tunnel.

Gophers are sometimes called pocket gophers because of two fur-lined pouches on either side of the mouth. The gophers use these pouches to carry food to special storage places in the tunnels. Gophers are herbivores, which means they eat only

plants. They feed mainly on roots and other underground parts of plants. Their coats range in color from white to brown to black. Gophers breed in the late spring. Females usually give birth to litters of between 2 and 11.

Since gophers destroy many roots, they are considered pests. Their tunnels, however, help aerate the soil and are rich in organic material. The name *gopher* is sometimes applied to a species of ground squirrel and to a type of tortoise.

GOPHER

Gophers make underground burrows, as shown by a Buller's gopher (above), which is digging in the soil with its sharp front teeth. The valley gopher (right) has cheek pouches, which it uses to carry food to storage places.

GORILLA

The gorilla is the largest of the apes. It lives in forests near the equator in Africa (see APE). This mammal has black skin. Except for the face and chest, the gorilla is covered with coarse, black hair. It has large, flaring nostrils and relatively small eyes. The male is often twice the size of the female, sometimes reaching a height of 6 ft. [1.8 m] and a weight of 440 lb. [200 kg]. Gorillas in captivity grow even larger. Some have weighed more than 605 lb. [275 kg]. The male has a bony crest on the top of the skull and a large, bony ridge over the eyes.

When a male is about ten years old, some of the hair on his back begins to change to a gray or silver color. For this reason, the older males are called silverbacks. Gorillas usually live in small groups led by a silverback. A group may contain several adult females, other adult males (blackbacks), and young gorillas and infants. Gorillas are called herbivores because they eat only plants. They usually eat during the day. Although they spend most of the time on the ground, gorillas may climb trees during the day for food or at night to sleep among the branches. Gorillas have no regular homes. They make a new sleeping place each night.

A gorilla rarely stands upright. It usually walks by supporting part of its weight on the knuckles of its hands. Gorillas sometimes beat their chests and grunt or scream loudly—probably to scare away intruders. In spite of their sometimes ferocious appearance, gorillas are actually shy, unaggressive animals. If disturbed, however, a gorilla may attack and kill an enemy. Gorillas are less curious and less intelligent than their relatives, the chimpanzees. However, gorillas are capable of solving simple problems.

After a pregnancy of 250 to 290 days, a female gorilla gives birth to a baby weighing about 4.4 lb. [2 kg]. Wild gorillas usually live for about 30 years.

There are three subspecies of gorillas. The mountain gorilla is considered rare. Its numbers have decreased because it is in great demand for zoos and medical research. In addition, much of its regular habitat has been destroyed by people. The other two subspecies, the western lowland gorilla and the eastern lowland gorilla, are slightly larger and much more numerous than the mountain gorilla.

GORILLA

An older male mountain gorilla is known as a silverback for the light-colored fur on its back. It is the largest of the apes. It usually walks on all fours, using its rear toes and front knuckles, although it can stand upright.

GOURD FAMILY The gourd family, Cucurbitaceae, is a plant group of dicotyledons that contains about 750 species (see DICOTYLEDON). They grow throughout the world, especially in the tropics. Gourds have large leaves and bell-shaped flowers with five petals. The gourd family includes many species of climbing plants. The pumpkin, squash, cucumber, melon, and watermelon all belong to the gourd family.

Ornamental gourds are attractive plants, often grown for display purposes. The dishcloth gourd, or luffa, has fruit that, when dried, is used in the making of artificial bath sponges and dishcloths. Many of the ornamental gourds are poisonous.

GOURD FAMILY

Gourds come in a wide range of shapes and sizes. The hard-shelled types shown here are often used as ornaments.

GOVERNOR A governor is a device that controls the speed of an engine. The power of an engine can vary for several reasons. Without a governor, these variations would cause the speed of the engine to vary as well. The first governor was built by the Scottish engineer, James Watt, in 1770. He used it in his invention of the steam engine (see WATT, JAMES).

There are three main types of governors: mechanical, electronic, and fluid. Mechanical governors operate by centrifugal force, a force that pushes an object that is moving in a circle outward from the center (see CENTRIPETAL FORCE). Most engines transmit their power by a rotating shaft. This shaft is made to rotate a number of balls, called flyballs or flyweights. As the shaft rotates faster, the balls are flung farther outward because of the centrifugal force. As they move outward, the balls start to close the throttle. The throttle controls the amount of fuel or steam entering the engine. If the throttle is partly closed, less steam or fuel enters the engine, and the engine slows down. When the engine slows down, the balls move inward. This opens the throttle, and more steam or fuel enters the engine.

In some large machines, governors cannot control the engine directly. In these cases, things called servomechanisms are used. The governors control the servomechanisms, which then control the engines.

See also ENGINE.

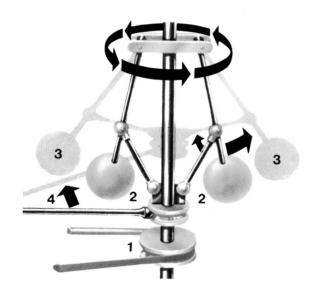

GOVERNOR

A governor controls the speed of an engine. The driving of a belt wheel (1) causes two balls (2) to rotate. As the engine speed increases, the balls move upward (3) and raise a lever (4), which reduces the fuel supply to the engine.

GRACKLE Grackles are long-billed birds that belong to the blackbird family, Icteridae (see BLACKBIRD). Although most of a grackle's body is black, there are highlights of purple and green present. There are two species of grackles in North America. The boat-tailed grackle is a large bird, growing to lengths of 16 in. [40 cm]. It is found in Mexico and the Atlantic coastal regions of the United States south of Virginia. Its tail is V-shaped, resembling a boat. The common grackle is found throughout the central and eastern United States and Canada. It can grow to 1 ft. [30 cm] in length. Grackles eat insects, grubs, and worms as well as grain.

GRACKLE

The greater Antillean grackle is a large member of the group. This bird was photographed in St. Lucia in the West Indies.

GRAND CANYON The Grand Canyon is a huge gorge in Arizona that was formed by erosion of the valley of the Colorado River (see EROSION). It is about 217 mi. [349 km] long and ranges from 4 to 18 mi. [7.5 to 29 km] across. In places, it is more than 1 mi. [1.6 km] deep. The Grand Canyon is famous around the world for its colorful rocks and majestic appearance.

For years, the Colorado River has slowly cut through the high plateaus of northern Arizona, exposing strata, or layers of rock, that are millions of years old. These strata are of great interest to geologists because they represent many years of the earth's history. At the bottom of the canyon, where the Colorado River flows, is ancient Precambrian rock that contains fossils of primitive algae. Fossils of dinosaurs, elephants, trees, and other past life are found in the higher strata. The most recent rocks occur near or at the top of the canyon. The sequence of fossils of the Grand Canyon provides an illustration of the evolutionary process (see EVOLUTION; FOSSIL; STRATIFICATION).

Each year, more than one million people view the Grand Canyon. In 1919, the United States government created Grand Canyon National Park, thus preserving the wealth of plant and animal life that has adapted to this unique environment.

GRANITE Granite is one of the most common of all rocks in the earth's crust. Mineralogically, granite consists mainly of feldspar and quartz. Sometimes, there are smaller amounts of other minerals, including hornblende and mica. Most granite is said to be coarse-grained. In other words, the crystals are large enough to be visible to the naked eye. The individual crystals in most granite measure from 0.06 to 0.5 in. [1.6 to 13 mm] in width. The quartz crystals are transparent or opaque (see CRYSTAL).

The feldspar crystals may be white, gray, or pink and duller in appearance than the quartz. The crystals of hornblende and mica are dark and sparkly. Most geologists believe that all granite was once melted rock, like lava (see LAVA). Unlike lava, however, it did not reach the earth's surface. It cooled and hardened deep under the ground. It cooled slowly, allowing large crystals to form as it hardened.

Because it is resistant to all forms of weather, granite is used in the construction of buildings, bridges, and monuments. Granite is quarried in more than half the states in the United States. Several other countries, such as Canada, Sweden, Scotland, and Finland, also quarry granite. Finland's red granite is desired for polished monuments because of its deep red color.
See also MINERAL; ROCK.

GRANITE
Granite is a hard rock that resists weathering. The design on this granite tombstone is just as sharp as when it was carved hundreds of years ago.

GRAPE Grapes are the fruit of climbing plants belonging to the vine family, Vitaceae (see VINE FAMILY). They are native to the Northern Hemisphere. Grapes have been cultivated for thousands of years. Eighty percent of the grapes grown are used in making wine. The rest are used for eating or to make juice, jelly, or raisins. About 66 million tons [60 million metric tons] of grapes are harvested each year.

There are two main types of grapes—the European grape and the North American grape. The European grape makes up about 95 percent of the world's grape supply. Italy, France, and Spain produce about half of this. In the 1500s, Spanish explorers brought the European grape to Mexico. California now produces the largest quantity of European grapes in the United States. They make fine wines because of their high sugar content (see FERMENTATION).

There are two main species of North American grapes: American bunch grapes and muscadine grapes. American bunch grapes are grown in the northeastern part of the United States, especially in New York. The popular Concord grape is of this variety and is used to make grape juice and jelly. The muscadine grape is grown in the southern part of the United States, from North Carolina to Texas.

GRAPE

Grapes are widely grown in warm regions for making wine—the juice of black grapes for red wine, and the juice of white grapes for white wine. Pink rosé wine is usually made from white grape juice with the fruit skins left in the juice.

GRAPEFRUIT Grapefruit is a large citrus fruit that is popular as a breakfast or salad fruit (see CITRUS FRUIT). It is closely related to the shaddock tree, or pummelo, of southeastern Asia. Its name comes from the fact that the wild fruit grows in clusters, like grapes. The grapefruit tree is among the largest that bears citrus fruit. It grows 15 to 40 ft. [5 to 12.2 m] high. Its flowers are large, white, and fragrant.

Grapefruit grows larger than the largest orange. Its smooth skin becomes bright yellow when ripe. The juicy flesh has a slightly bitter taste. Grapefruit is picked by hand and handled very carefully to prevent bruising. Grapefruit is an excellent source of vitamin C.

About 67 percent of the world's grapefruit crops are grown in the United States. The state of Florida produces about 60 million boxes of grapefruit each year. Each box contains 60 lb. [36 kg] of grapefruit. Florida's production accounts for 75 percent of the U.S. crop. Texas, California, and Arizona are other states that grow grapefruit. Other countries that grow grapefruit are Argentina, China, Cyprus, Israel, and South Africa. The grapefruit tree thrives in warm climates. It grows only in frost-free areas.

Grapefruit is thought to have been first cultivated in the West Indies in the 1700s. Around 1820, grapefruit was brought to Florida from the West Indies. It was not marketed in the United States outside of Florida until after 1900. Northern people, who had eaten grapefruit during vacations in Florida, began creating a demand for the fruit.

Some grapefruits have no seeds and are called seedless grapefruit. They do not have as good a flavor as grapefruit with seeds but are popular because they are easy to prepare. The chief commercial seedless variety is called marsh. Pink grapefruit is a variety that has pink-colored flesh due to altered genes (see GENE). However, its flesh tastes the same as the regular yellow-fleshed varieties. Thompson is another popular variety. Grapefruit has been crossed with the tangerine to produce a fruit called tangelo.

GRAPEFRUIT

Ripe grapefruit are eaten for breakfast or in fruit salad, but most of the commercial crop is used for making grapefruit juice, popular as a refreshing drink.

GRAPH A graph is a drawing or diagram that shows how two quantities are related to each other. For example, a graph can be used to show the height of a rocket above the ground during the first seven seconds of its flight. The information from which the graph is made is shown in the table below:

Time (seconds)	0	1	2	3	4	5	6	7
Height (meters)	0	10	25	50	85	115	135	150
(feet)	0	32.8	82	164	279	377	443	492

This information is graphed by drawing a pair of lines called axes. Intervals of time are marked on one axis. Intervals of height are marked on the other. The horizontal axis is often called the *x*-axis. The vertical axis is often called the *y*-axis. Each pair of numbers in the table can be shown by one point on the graph. For example, point A shows that, after 4 seconds, the rocket was about 85 meters up. Joining the points to form a smooth curve makes it possible to find heights at times between those plotted on the graph. As shown in the graph, it can be read that, after 4.5 seconds, the rocket reached 100 meters.

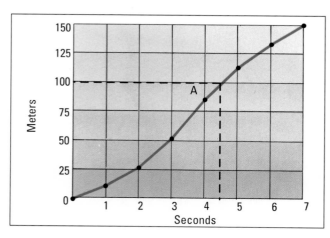

If the two quantities are related by a formula, the graph is a straight line or a regular curve. The formula is the equation of the line (see ALGEBRA).

For example, the breaking strength of a particular type of rope is given by the equation $L = 200d(d+1)$. The symbol L stands for the number of grams or pounds that will snap a rope d centimeters or inches in diameter. This relationship is plotted by first making a table listing various values of d and the corresponding values of L, based on the above formula.

d (centimeters)	0	1	2	3	4
(Inches)	0	0.39	0.78	1.17	1.56
L (grams)	0	400	1,200	2,400	4,000
(pounds)	0	0.88	2.64	5.29	8.8

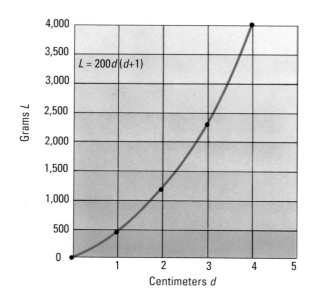

In statistics, bar graphs are often used instead of line graphs. The table and graph below show the average monthly rainfall in a Midwestern city.

Month	Jan	Feb	Mar	Apr	May	Jun	Jul	Aug	Sep	Oct	Nov	Dec
Rainfall (centimeters)	10.9	7.9	7.1	5.6	6.1	5.3	4.4	4.6	2.2	8.5	10.2	11.4
Rainfall (inches)	4.3	3.1	2.8	2.2	2.4	2.1	1.7	1.8	0.9	3.3	4.0	4.5

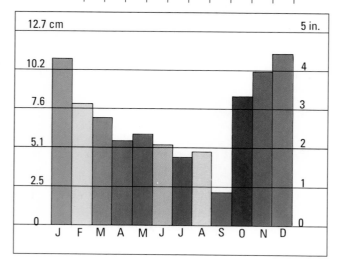

Many other types of graphs picture a wide range of subjects. Graphs are often used to show a basic trend to make certain facts plain, instead of giving complex statistics. Today, computers produce elaborate, detailed graphs for science and business and industry.

GRAPHITE Graphite is one of the softest minerals known. A form of carbon, graphite is black or bluish gray with a metallic luster and a greasy feel. It occurs in igneous and metamorphic rocks, such as schist and marble (see CARBON; MINERAL; ROCK). Graphite deposits occur in twenty-five states in the United States. However, the leading graphite producers are China, Mexico, Korea, and Austria.

Although graphite is very soft, it is the same element as diamond, the hardest natural material. Graphite forms in very thin, flat crystals. Crystals are groups of atoms arranged in a certain order. In the carbon crystals, the groups of atoms are tightly bound together in layers. However, each layer is only weakly connected to the next and they slip past each other easily. This effect gives graphite the properties of feeling soft and greasy (see CRYSTAL).

Manufacturers harden graphite with clay to produce the substance in pencils commonly (but incorrectly) called lead. Graphite has many other uses in addition to its use in pencils. Because graphite conducts electricity and does not burn, electrodes made of graphite work under conditions that would destroy metal electrodes (see ELECTRODE). Graphite also conducts heat. It does not combine with other chemicals except at very high temperatures. Many crucibles are made from graphite. Crucibles are containers in which metal is melted.

Because graphite is not easily dissolved, it is used to line tanks that hold strong acids. Also, the inner parts of some nuclear reactors are made of bricks of graphite.

The property of having a greasy or slippery feel makes graphite a good lubricant for clocks and other machines with small parts. Graphite is also used as the raw material in making synthetic diamonds.

GRASS Grass is any of about ten thousand widely varied species of flowering plants belonging to the family Poaceae. Grasses are monocotyledons. Most are herbaceous plants, though a few species, such as bamboos, are woody plants (see HERBACEOUS PLANT; MONOCOTYLEDON; WOODY PLANT). The grass family is one of the largest and most widespread of all plant families. Grasses are used as food, as shelter for wildlife, as construction materials, and as a source of various drugs. Most grasses produce a dense network of fibrous roots, which binds the soil together to prevent erosion (see EROSION).

Most grasses are perennial, which means they live for several years. Some grasses, however, last only one year; they are known as annual plants. Except during the flowering season, the stems, called culms, remain short and close to the ground. Only the leaves grow upwards, and because they grow from the base, the grass plants are not usually harmed by repeated mowing or grazing. Often, the culms send out many sideshoots, allowing a single plant to cover a large area in a short amount of time. When neighboring plants join, they form a turf. These stems, if underground, are called rhizomes (see RHIZOME). Bermuda grass grows by means of rhizomes. If the stems are above the surface, they are called stolons or tillers.

Most grasses flower early in the summer, when some stems grow rapidly upwards and soon grow above the leaves. The flowers are in little oval spikelets at the tops of these stems. Each spikelet consists of a number of small scales surrounding one or more simple flowers. Each flower is small and green, with no petals and no scent or nectar—

ACTIVITY *What does graphite feel like?*

Take an ordinary lead pencil and rub it on a sheet of paper until you get an even black surface. Rub your finger on this surface. See how greasy it feels. Now rub your fintertips together. Do they feel slippery? This shows how well graphite acts as a lubricant, and why it is used to make things slide over one another.

GRASS

Ornamental grasses, such as the pampas type (top), are often grown for their decorative two-colored leaves. Rye grass (bottom) is the wild ancestor of a cultivated cereal grass whose grain is used for making flour and whiskey.

just a pistil and two or three long-stalked stamens that sway and scatter pollen in the breeze. The spikelets may be tightly clustered on the stem, as in an ear of wheat, or widely spaced on slender branches (see FLOWER).

There are six major economic groups of grasses. Grazing grasses provide food for livestock and other grazing animals. Redtop grass is a popular grazing grass that is often processed into hay. Turf grasses are used to cover lawns, golf courses, and athletic fields. Kentucky bluegrass and Bermuda grass are two popular varieties. Ornamental grasses are usually grown for their colorful and decorative leaves and flowers. Cereal grasses, such as wheat, rice, corn, rye, and oats, are a major food source. Sugar cane supplies more than half the world's sugar. Woody grasses, such as bamboo, supply many useful items for construction.

See also CEREAL CROP.

GRASSHOPPER Grasshoppers are leaping insects belonging to the order Orthoptera. There are over 10,000 species, living in a wide range of environments throughout the world. They vary widely in size, the largest being about 3.5 in. [9 cm] long.

The head of a grasshopper is broad and blunt. Two fairly short antennae give the grasshopper its sense of smell and touch (see ANTENNAE). The mouth is made of two hard lips and two sharp, biting jaws. The sense of taste comes from tiny, fingerlike buds around the mouth. There are two compound eyes, which are used for vision, and three simple eyes, which probably only detect light (see EYE AND VISION).

The legs and wings are attached to the thorax (see ABDOMEN; THORAX). Usually, two tough forewings cover two thin hindwings, which are used for flying. Some grasshoppers have vestigial wings or no wings at all (see VESTIGIAL ORGAN). All six legs are used for walking. The two rear legs are much larger and stronger and allow a grasshopper to jump great distances. Grasshoppers can jump as far as 6.6 ft. [2 m]. Most of them are green or brown.

The thorax has two pairs and the abdomen has eight pairs of spiracles. These are holes that are used in breathing. The female grasshopper lays batches of eggs in the late summer or fall or, in the tropics, several times a year. The eggs are covered with a mucuslike substance that hardens into a pod. The pod, usually buried in the ground, protects the eggs during the winter. The eggs hatch into nymphs that look like small, wingless adults. After molting five to eight times, the nymphs develop into adults.

This is an example of incomplete metamorphosis (see METAMORPHOSIS; MOLTING). Males and sometimes females "sing" by rubbing their rear legs against their forewings. This method of sound production is called stridulation. It is performed only in the sunshine.

Grasshoppers are herbivores (plant eaters). They feed mostly on leafy plants and grasses. They cause about 30 million dollars' worth of damage to crops each year. For this reason, farmers often spray their fields with insecticides. Some flies that lay their eggs in the egg-containing pod are major natural enemies of grasshoppers. Other natural enemies include frogs, snakes, spiders, birds, beetles, and parasitic wasps. In some countries, grasshoppers are captured and eaten as food.

Some grasshoppers are called locusts (see LOCUST). Locusts are usually brown or green, though some species are red or yellow. As the population of locusts increases, crowding may occur. The locusts then swarm and migrate in search of food. Swarms of locusts cause extensive damage to crops. They have long been feared by the superstitious as an omen, or sign, of evil.

The bush crickets and katydids are often called long-horned grasshoppers because of their very long, thin antennae, which are often much longer than the body. But they are not true grasshoppers and they belong to a different family of the Orthoptera. Most of them are green or brown and they usually live in bushes, whereas most grasshoppers live in the grass. Unlike the true grasshoppers, the bush crickets and katydids eat a lot of insects. Some of the bigger species, which may be over 6 in. [15 cm] long, are entirely carnivorous. The males and some females produce sounds by stridulation, but they rub the bases of their forewings together instead of rubbing their legs against their wings. Unlike the true grasshoppers, many of these insects sing at night. The females lay their eggs in the ground or in plant stems after making holes with a swordlike or bladelike ovipositor.

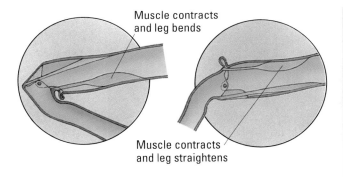

Muscle contracts and leg bends

Muscle contracts and leg straightens

GRASSHOPPER—Jumping legs

A grasshopper jumps into the air by rapidly straightening its back legs, powered by a pair of muscles (above). The back legs are much longer and stronger than its other legs (far right).

GRASSHOPPER—Defense

The mottled stone grasshopper (far left) is hard to spot when it is at rest on the ground. But when disturbed (left), it flashes its pink hind-wings to startle an attacker such as a bird.

GRAVITY

If you throw a ball straight up in the air, it eventually starts to slow down. Then it will stop and begin to fall back to the ground. As it falls, it moves slowly at first and then picks up speed. The ball falls to the ground because it is pulled downward by the force of gravity.

The English scientist Sir Isaac Newton was the first person to understand what was happening. He explained it in his laws of motion (see DYNAMICS;

NEWTON, SIR ISAAC). Newton's first law states that a moving body continues moving with the same velocity (speed in a certain direction) unless acted on by a force (see FORCE). In other words, its speed and its direction of motion stay the same unless something acts upon them. When a ball is thrown into the air, its speed changes. It slows down. Its direction also changes as it starts to fall back to the ground. Newton realized that this is due to the force of gravity. He also realized that the same force keeps the moon in orbit around the earth. As the moon moves around the earth, its direction of travel is always changing. Therefore, he thought, there is a force between the earth and the moon. This is also the force of gravity. He realized that a force of gravity exists between all matter.

Newton discovered a number of properties of gravity. Gravity obeys the inverse square law. The farther apart two bodies are, the weaker is the force between them. If the bodies are twice as far apart, the force is four times as weak. The force of gravity also depends on the masses of the two bodies. If

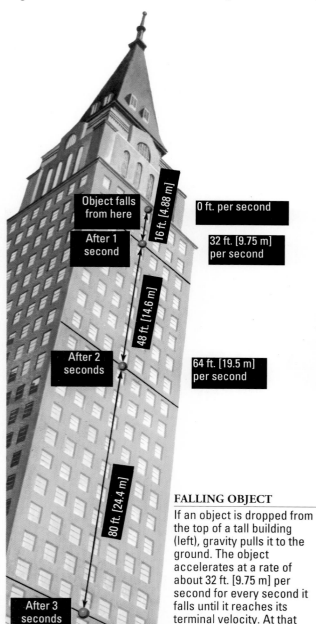

Object falls from here

After 1 second

16 ft. [4.88 m]

0 ft. per second

32 ft. [9.75 m] per second

48 ft. [14.6 m]

After 2 seconds

64 ft. [19.5 m] per second

80 ft. [24.4 m]

After 3 seconds

96 ft. [29.3 m] per second

FALLING OBJECT

If an object is dropped from the top of a tall building (left), gravity pulls it to the ground. The object accelerates at a rate of about 32 ft. [9.75 m] per second for every second it falls until it reaches its terminal velocity. At that point, air resistance balances out the pull of gravity, and the object falls at a constant speed.

TIDES

Gravity is the force of attraction between two objects because of their mass. The gravitational force between the moon and the water in the earth's oceans causes tides. The force pulls the water into a bulge on the side of the earth facing the moon, causing a high tide in that region. As the earth rotates on its axis, the bulge moves to another place. The effect is best seen in a tidal river estuary at high tide (top) and low tide (bottom).

either mass is doubled, then the force between them is doubled. If both masses are doubled, then the force is four times as strong (see MASS).

On the moon's surface, the force of gravity is about six times as weak as on Earth. For this reason, a human being weighs six times less on the moon than on the earth (see WEIGHT). A person weighing 132 lb. [60 kg] on earth weighs about 22 lb. [10 kg] on the moon. Weight depends on the pull of gravity.

When either the speed or the direction of motion of a body changes, it accelerates (see ACCELERATION). Like other forces, gravity causes bodies to accelerate. An object falling toward the ground is accelerating. It will do so until friction caused by the air prevents further acceleration (see FRICTION). The acceleration is the same for all falling bodies (if we ignore air friction). It does not depend on their masses. Acceleration on the earth is just over 32 ft. [9.75 m] per second for every second that an object falls. This means that after one second, a falling body is moving at about 32 ft. [9.75 m] per second. After two seconds, its speed is about 64 ft. [20 m] per second, and so on.

Gravity is now explained by the theory of relativity. This theory was introduced by the physicist Albert Einstein (see EINSTEIN, ALBERT; RELATIVITY). Relativity explains the properties of gravity very accurately. Newton's theory is still used, however, because it is much simpler. Its results are still satisfactory for the work of most scientists and engineers.

MASS AND WEIGHT

An astronaut's weight on the moon is only about one sixth of the person's weight on the earth. The person's mass remains the same, but weight changes because the moon's gravity is about one sixth of the earth's. The astronaut could jump six times as high—and six times as far—on the moon as on the earth.

ACTIVITY *Dropping weights*

You can do a simple experiment to prove that gravity makes all objects fall at the same rate. Stand with your arms stretched out sideways at shoulder height. Hold a small pebble in one hand and a larger stone in the other hand. Let go of the stones at exactly the same time. Have a friend check when the stones hit the ground. You will find that they land at the same time, even though they have different weights.

GREAT BARRIER REEF The Great Barrier Reef is the world's largest coral reef. It stretches 1,250 mi. [2,012 km] along the coast of Queensland, Australia (see CORAL).

Geologists think that the coral formations grew in shallow waters on slowly sinking land. The land is now covered by the sea. The changes in sea level have helped the growth of coral.

Since the 1960s, the crown-of-thorns starfish has been eating the living coral, thus preventing the formation of new reef areas.

Great Barrier Reef

Australia

GREAT BARRIER REEF

The Great Barrier Reef lies off northeast Australia (left). It is made of coral (above), which will grow only in the shallow warm waters over the reef. It provides homes for many fish, crustaceans, and mollusks, though recently the coral has been attacked by starfish.

GREAT CIRCLE A great circle is a circle that divides a sphere into equal halves. Any number of different circles can be drawn on the surface of a sphere. These circles all divide the surface into two areas. There is one group of circles that divides the sphere into two equal halves. These circles are the great circles. For example, the equator around the earth divides the earth into the Northern Hemisphere and the Southern Hemisphere. These two hemispheres are equal. Therefore, the equator is a great circle. One way to determine a great circle is to identify the largest circle that can be drawn on the surface of a sphere.

GREBE Grebes are water birds that belong to the family Podicipedidae. From a distance, they look like ducks. However, a grebe has a longer neck and a narrower bill than a duck has. Grebes do not fly well, but they are excellent swimmers. They catch their food—small water animals—by diving underwater. They spend the summers on inland lakes and most species fly to the coast for the winters. There are six species in North America. *See also* BIRD.

GREENHOUSE EFFECT *Greenhouse effect* is the term for the natural process by which the earth's atmosphere absorbs some of the sun's energy, warming the earth. The greenhouse effect also occurs on other planets besides Earth. Many scientists feel this effect is intensifying on Earth and could lead to serious environmental problems.

Most of the light from the sun passes through the earth's atmosphere, warming the earth and providing the light necessary for photosynthesis (see ATMOSPHERE; PHOTOSYNTHESIS). The earth's surface sends some of the heat energy back into the atmosphere. However, the heat does not pass through the atmosphere as easily as light does. Gases in the atmosphere, such as carbon dioxide, absorb much of the heat. This heat is radiated back to the earth, causing the greenhouse effect (see CARBON DIOXIDE).

Some scientists believe that pollution in the atmosphere is causing abnormal amounts of heat to be absorbed (see POLLUTION). A main cause of this pollution is exhaust produced by the internal combustion engines in automobiles. The exhaust contains carbon dioxide, a "greenhouse gas." Carbon dioxide is also released into the atmosphere from other sources. Homes and industry burn fossil fuels, such as coal and oil, for energy. This process releases huge amounts of carbon dioxide into the atmosphere (see FOSSIL FUEL). Another factor in the increase of carbon dioxide is the cutting down of rain forests in South America and elsewhere. Here, the carbon dioxide in the atmosphere is increased in two ways. First, rain forests are often cleared by burning, which releases carbon dioxide. Second, green plants in the rain forests use carbon dioxide during the process of photosynthesis. A decrease in rain forests then means that less carbon dioxide is being taken out of the atmosphere (see RAIN FOREST).

Scientists estimate that the amount of carbon dioxide in the atmosphere has almost doubled since the 1850s. Many feel this is causing the temperature of the earth to rise. Some scientists refer to the rise in temperature as *global warming*. In 1995 it was observed that, in the Northern Hemisphere, spring flowers were blooming 10 days earlier than they were in the 1890s, and some birds were nesting and frogs spawning two weeks earlier than they were in the 1960s. A rising temperature could have serious consequences. For example, it might cause shifts in precipitation patterns and unstable weather due to the interaction of a warm atmosphere and a polar ice cap. A decrease in precipitation might mean that important agricultural areas would turn to deserts. Many organisms might not

be able to adapt and would die off, affecting the food chain (see AGRICULTURE; FOOD CHAIN). The ice at the North and South poles might melt, causing the oceans to rise. Scientists do not know exactly how high the oceans would rise. However, even a moderate rise would cause widespread flooding in many parts of the world. Many cities and agricultural areas would be threatened.

There is disagreement among scientists, however, over how much the greenhouse effect is actually intensifying. There is also disagreement over what should be done about the problem. For example, some scientists feel that the way to reduce the amount of carbon dioxide being released is to replace electric-power plants that burn fossil fuels with plants that use nuclear energy (see NUCLEAR ENERGY). Other scientists say that the risks of a serious accident at a nuclear plant is too great to justify the switch. The result of this uncertainty is that world leaders are hesitant to take any preventive measures without more firm scientific information.

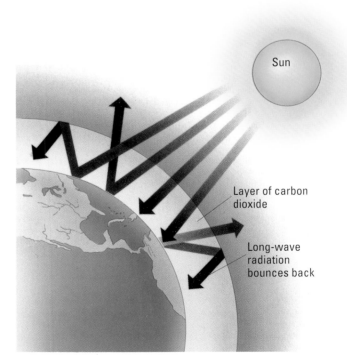

GREENHOUSE EFFECT

Much of the incoming light radiation from the sun is absorbed by the land and oceans, then sent back as radiation of a longer wavelength. A layer of gases such as carbon dioxide in the upper atmosphere reflects this radiation, which bounces back to Earth and makes it warmer. This is the greenhouse effect.

GREENWICH MEAN TIME

Greenwich (grĭn' ĭch) mean time, abbreviated GMT, is the standard time for the British Isles and western Europe. Greenwich mean time is the local time at Greenwich, in England, through which the prime meridian passes. The prime meridian is at 0° longitude. Time zones are measured east or west of Greenwich. Time zones to the east of Greenwich are one hour ahead of GMT for every 15° of longitude. Time zones west of Greenwich are one hour behind Greenwich for every 15° of longitude.

See also LATITUDE AND LONGITUDE; TIME ZONE.

GRINDING AND POLISHING

Grinding and polishing are common processes used to produce a certain shape, size, smoothness, or roughness on various types of products. Both processes use abrasives, which are substances that cause surfaces to be worn away. Grinding uses abrasives to remove material. Polishing uses abrasives to make surfaces of materials smoother (see ABRASIVE).

Grinding

Grinding is one of the earliest known manufacturing processes. In prehistoric times, people shaped stone tools by rubbing them against harder, abrasive stones.

Much grinding today is done by abrasive wheels that rotate at high speed. Some grinding is done by power-driven belts of cloth or paper. The cloth or paper is coated with an abrasive. Grinding wheels come in many different sizes. Wheels with coarse grains are used for rough grinding. Medium wheels are used for general sharpening. Fine wheels are used for grinding those products that must have a very smooth surface.

Various cementing materials bond the abrasive grains together in a wheel. One of the most common abrasives is silicon carbide. Silicon carbide is used for grinding hard, brittle materials such as cast iron. Alumina, also called aluminum oxide, is a tougher abrasive used for tool steel and wrought iron. In many wheels, clay is the bonding material that holds such abrasives together. The clay is mixed with the abrasive material and then heated. Plastic resins and rubber also may be used as the bonding materials (see RESIN). Grinding belts use the same abrasives as wheels. Belts grind metals, glass, and ceramics.

Various methods are used in grinding. In offhand grinding, the worker holds the material against the rotating wheel or belt. This type of grinding is commonly used to sharpen knives and drills and also to remove roughness from various metal objects. Surface grinding machines may have the axis of the wheel either horizontal or vertical to the surface of the work. Surface grinding produces a smooth, flat surface on machine parts, tools, and dies. Cylindrical grinding is used to produce a very accurate finishing surface on shafts, pistons, and other similarly shaped machine parts. Abrasive wheel cutting uses a narrow wheel. The material is usually bonded with rubber. Such wheels rotate at very high speeds. They are constantly flooded with liquid to control the heat produced by the tool or other object being ground.

Polishing

Polishing is usually done with wheels made of leather, felt, or other cloth. These materials are coated with a very fine abrasive, such as a fine grade of silicon carbide or alumina. In extremely fine polishing, jewelers' rouge, a fine, dark red oxide of iron, or tripoli, a type of silica, may be used.

Abrasive belts are used in some kinds of polishing. Polishing wheels made of soft rubber are also used. However, most polishing on oddly shaped pieces is done by hand. High-speed machines are used for large-scale operations, such as finishing large sheets of stainless steel.

GRIZZLY BEAR

The grizzly bear is a large bear that is considered to be a subspecies or race of the brown bear (see BROWN BEAR). The grizzly bear has heavy brown fur with silver tips, giving the coat a grizzled appearance. This is how the grizzly bear got its name. The grizzly bear may be as tall as 8.3 ft. [2.5 m] when standing up on its back legs, and may weigh more than 990 lb. [450 kg]. It has long, curved claws that it uses to dig into the burrows of small rodents. The grizzly bear is an omnivore and eats small mammals, fish, plants, and honey.

The reputation of the grizzly bear as a fierce and

vicious animal is largely undeserved. Like most other bears, the grizzly bear prefers to avoid trouble. Its gentle mood changes rapidly, however, if it is threatened or if it must defend its cubs or home. Grizzly bears once roamed throughout western North America. Hunters have greatly reduced the numbers of these bears, however, and the grizzly bear may be on its way to extinction (see EXTINCTION). The grizzly bears that are alive today live near the Rocky Mountains. Most of them live in Alaska and Canada and in Yellowstone and Glacier national parks. The grizzly appears on the state flag of California as a symbol of determination.

GRIZZLY BEAR
The grizzly bear gets its name from its silver-tipped brown fur, which can look gray. (*Grizzly* is an old word meaning "gray.") Alaskan grizzlies are the largest meat-eating animals that live on land.

GROSBEAK Grosbeak is a name given to several big-billed songbirds that belong to the finch family, Fringillidae (see FINCH). There are five such species in North America: the rose-breasted, black-headed, blue, evening, and pine grosbeaks. All are plump, colorful birds with short, thick bills. The heavy bills are used for cracking seeds, their favorite food. Grosbeaks grow to 7.25 in. [18 cm] in length.

GROUNDHOG The groundhog, also called the woodchuck, is a rodent belonging to the squirrel family (see MARMOT; SQUIRREL). It lives in Canada and the eastern half of the United States. Groundhogs are about 2 ft. [61 cm] in length and have a bushy tail. Their brownish fur is rather coarse.

Groundhogs live in the woods and open fields, where they build complex underground burrows. They hibernate in the burrows during winter (see HIBERNATION). Groundhogs feed on a wide range of plants during the day. Their feeding sometimes damages fruit and other crops.

GROUNDWATER Groundwater is water that exists beneath the earth's surface. The earth contains about 2 million cu. mi. [8.3 million cu. km] of groundwater. Groundwater is usually found down to 3,000 ft. [915 m] beneath the surface. Below this level, the pressure of the earth squeezes and seals the rocks so that no water can penetrate. There are three main types of groundwater: meteoric, juvenile, and connate.

Meteoric water makes up most groundwater. This is the water that seeps underground from precipitation or from the bottoms of lakes and rivers (see PRECIPITATION). Juvenile water forms by chemical processes that occur in rocks far beneath the earth's surface. Meteoric and juvenile water are fresh water. Connate water is salt water seeping from rocks that once lay beneath ancient seas.

Groundwater is held beneath the earth's surface in an area called the zone of saturation. The top of the zone of saturation is known as the water table. The water table rises and falls depending on the amount of precipitation. As the water table rises, it is said to be recharging. Water from precipitation filters to the zone of saturation through the zone of aeration. Collections of water in porous underground rocks in the zone of saturation are called aquifers (see AQUIFER). Groundwater reaches the surface through openings called springs. Spring water is usually cold, but there are springs with hot water, called geysers (see SPRING AND GEYSER).

Many communities, farms, and industries get their water supply from groundwater. Falling water tables are a serious problem in many areas and have led to water shortages. Falling water tables are due to overuse by heavily populated communities and by farmers. Overuse of groundwater in coastal areas has caused another problem—contamination of existing groundwater. Ocean water has seeped in to replace the fresh water that has been used up. This

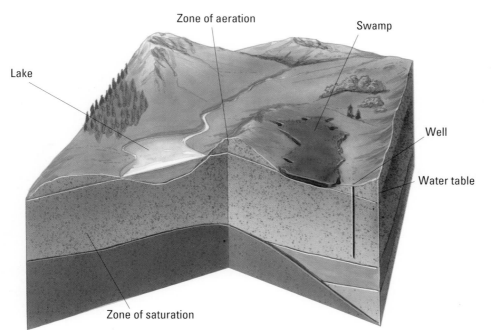

Lake

Zone of aeration

Swamp

Well

Water table

Zone of saturation

GROUNDWATER
Many communities, farms, and industries get their water supply from groundwater. To do this, wells are drilled into the zone of saturation.

makes the existing fresh water salty and unfit to drink. This seepage is called saltwater intrusion.

Groundwater has also been contaminated by chemicals. The sources of these chemicals include landfills, sewage from cities, underground waste-disposal sites, and underground gasoline-storage tanks that have leaks.

See also POLLUTION; WASTE DISPOSAL; WATER.

GROUPER A grouper is a saltwater fish that is a member of the sea bass family, Serranidae (see BASS). Most groupers live in temperate or tropical waters. There are over a dozen species found off the coasts of North America. Although a few groupers are only a few inches long, most are large fish, some growing to 6 ft. [2 m] in length.

GROUSE Grouse are chickenlike birds that belong to the family Tetraonidae. They live in forests and mountain grasslands of northern climates. There are many species of grouse in North America, including the prairie chickens and ptarmigans. Most grouse are popular game birds, highly prized for their flavor. They feed on berries, seeds, buds, and leaves. The best-known species, the ruffed grouse, has an unusual courtship ritual. The male stands on a dead log and beats his wings rapidly. This makes a loud "drumming" noise that carries through the forest. The purpose is to attract the female grouse. Grouse differ from other game birds in having feathers all over their legs.

See also BIRD.

GROUPER
The coral grouper is a large fish that preys on other fishes in the waters around tropical coral reefs.

GROUSE
The male prairie chicken, a type of grouse, inflates its golden air sacs in courtship display.

Growth is an irreversible increase in volume. All living things grow. A human being starts life as a single fertilized cell about 0.004 in. [0.1 mm] in diameter. Nine months later, when the baby is born, it weighs about 6 to 8 lb. [2.7 to 3.6 kg]. It may be from about 19 to 21 in. [48 to 53 cm] in length. When fully grown, an adult human male may be over 6 ft. [1.8 m] tall and weigh more than 170 lb. [77 kg]. Some living things show an even greater increase in size. A whale egg is microscopic. A full-grown whale, however, may be more than 100 ft. [30 m] in length. It may weigh about 160,000 lb. [72,600 kg]. A redwood may grow from a seed 0.06 in. [1.6 mm] in diameter to a tree over 300 ft. [91 m] in height.

Living organisms are made up of cells. Each living thing begins life as a single cell. The cell takes in materials. It uses these materials to construct cellular components and to fuel cellular processes. This cell can multiply and divide to make other cells. This process of building, multiplying, and dividing is responsible for growth (see CELL; MITOSIS).

In most organisms, as the cells grow, they change in character. They develop into specialized cells, such as nerve cells, skin cells, and bone cells.

This process is called differentiation (see DIFFERENTIATION, CELLULAR). The process of differentiation follows specific rules. Differentiation of cells is controlled by the genes. It is part of heredity (see HEREDITY). As growth occurs, certain cells develop that produce specific substances called hormones (see HORMONE). Hormones influence and regulate the further development of the organism.

Some nonliving things also increase in size. Rocks, for example, can increase in size. Some scientists consider this a form of growth. In nonliving things, however, there are no cells. The growth of a rock or mineral is growth by what is known as accretion. For example, water dripping from the ceiling of a cave leaves behind tiny mineral particles. These particles cling together. After hundreds of years, they form great bodies of stone (see STALACTITE AND STALAGMITE).

The various parts of an organism do not grow at the same speed. In plants, for example, growth generally takes place only behind the tips of roots and shoots, or in a layer called the cambium. Cells formed by the cambium increase the thickness of a tree's trunk and branches, forming the annual rings (see ANNUAL RING). In animals, the fertilized

INSECT GROWTH

Many insects, such as butterflies and moths, undergo several changes of form (metamorphosis) while growing from a newly hatched caterpillar into an adult. Other insects, such as crickets, grow steadily, molting, or shedding, between each stage, or instar.

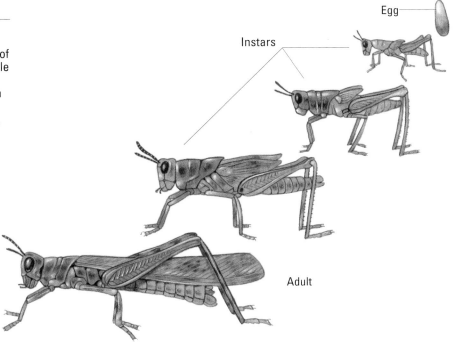

Egg

Instars

Adult

CELL DIVISION

Plants and animals grow by increasing their number of cells. Cells double in number by dividing in two in a process called mitosis, shown below.

Chromosomes

Spindle

Nucleus

Chromosomes

Chromosomes separate

New nucleus

Two daughter cells

TREE GROWTH

All trees, even the giant sequoia, begin life as tiny seeds. It takes hundreds of years for a year-old seedling to grow into a mature tree, which produces seed-bearing cones to repeat the process.

egg at first grows into a ball of cells. Different rates of growth of various parts of this ball cause the development of the creature's characteristic body shape. Some animals change their body shape completely between the egg and adult stage (see METAMORPHOSIS).

Even after birth, growth rates of various parts of the body may differ. In a human child, the arms and legs increase in length much more rapidly than the torso and head. Plants and some animals can regrow a part that is lost. This process is called regeneration (see REGENERATION). A person cannot regrow a lost finger. A lizard, however, can regrow a lost tail. As mentioned before, certain hormones are known to influence growth. Plant hormones are called auxins. In mammals, including humans, growth hormone is produced by the pituitary gland.

See also EMBRYO.

GRUNION The grunion—or California grunion—is a saltwater fish that belongs to the silverside family, Atherinidae. It lives in the Pacific Ocean off California.

The grunion is a small fish, averaging 6 in. [15 cm] in length. It spawns in large numbers on beaches along the ocean. Spawning takes place during the highest tide of the month. The female lays her eggs in the moist sand.
See also FISH; SPAWNING.

GUANACO The guanaco (*Lama guanacoe*) is a small, humpless member of the camel family. An adult guanaco is about 43 in. [110 cm] tall at the shoulder. It weighs as much as 43.6 lb. [96 kg]. It is covered with long, thick, woolly hair.

Guanacos are usually found in small herds of four to ten females led by one male. Guanacos live on the mountains, plateaus, and plains of South America. Females have a pregnancy of about ten to eleven months and normally have one young every other year.

Guanacos spit when they are annoyed. Some scientists think that llamas may be descended from guanacos.
See also LLAMA.

GUANACO
The guanaco is a South American ruminant (cud-chewing) mammal closely related to the domestic llama. It roams wild in small herds on the mountains and plains.

GUANO Guano is the dung of seabirds, bats, and seals. It makes an excellent fertilizer because of its phosphate and nitrate content.

Most of the world's supply of guano comes from the islands off the coast of Peru and from Baja California, where huge colonies of seabirds deposit tons of it every year. Bird guano is more valuable than bat or seal guano because it has a higher concentration of phosphate and nitrate. Bat guano is found mainly in caves.

GUINEA PIG The guinea pig is actually a rodent belonging to the family Caviidae (see RODENT). Guinea pigs come from South America, where the ancient Incas raised them for their meat. The common domestic guinea pig is a popular pet. It is about 10 in. [25 cm] long and it weighs about 1 lb. [0.5 kg]. It eats grass and other green plants and does not require very much water. The guinea pig has small legs and ears and no external tail. Many different breeds and colors of guinea pigs have been developed by scientists and breeders.

GUINEA PIG
Guinea pigs make popular pets. The type called Abyssinian, shown above, is noted for its long fur.

GULF STREAM The Gulf Stream is the fast-moving warm current of water in the North Atlantic Ocean. It flows from the Gulf of Mexico, through the Straits of Florida (where it is known as the Florida Current), northwards along the east

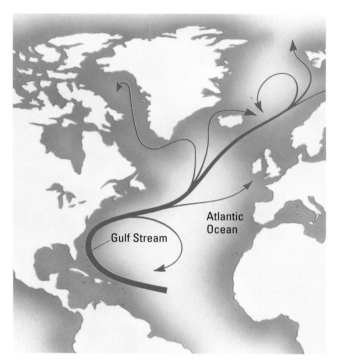

GULF STREAM
The Gulf Stream is a warm ocean current that flows northwestwards into the North Atlantic before swinging eastward to reach the shores of Europe.

coast of North America, and then northeastwards across the Atlantic to the northwestern coast of Europe. It is the warm part of the North Atlantic gyre—the general clockwise circulation of ocean water from the warm regions near the equator to the cold regions near the pole and back again. This whole system is driven by the trade winds that blow toward the southwest in the Northern Hemisphere. The surface water of the ocean is driven westwards along the equator by these winds, until it reaches a continent. There it spreads north and south along the continent's edge. The northward-spreading water forms the Gulf Stream.

The Gulf Stream can move at speeds of five knots, which is fast for an ocean current. It is a current of surface water, but off Cape Hatteras, North Carolina, its influence can be felt down to depths of 3,300 ft. [1,000 m]. The main part of the Gulf Stream is about 40 mi. [64 km] wide. In some places it breaks up into swirls and eddies, or whirlpools, that can be 150 mi. [240 km] across, with the water flowing out and around, and back into the main current again.

When the warm waters of the Gulf Stream meet the colder waters of the Labrador Current near Newfoundland, fog banks are formed (see FOG). These fog banks, added to the hazard of icebergs drifting southwards from Greenland, make this a very dangerous area for shipping. The mixture of warm and cold water here brings up nutrient-rich water from deep down in the ocean, feeding masses of algae that in turn feed fish. This is the origin of the important fishing grounds of the Grand Banks.

Further north, the Gulf Stream brings warm moist climates to local coastal areas, giving rise, for example, to palm trees in the western peninsulas of Scotland.

See also OCEAN; OCEANOGRAPHY; WIND.

GULL Gulls are large seabirds that belong to the family Laridae. There are about forty species in the world, with twenty species found in North America. Gulls are usually white with gray or black wings. Some species grow to 24 in. [60 cm] in length with wingspans of 65 in. [162 cm]. Gulls, also called seagulls, are very strong fliers. They are commonly seen soaring along the coasts. They are scavengers and will eat just about anything. The best-known gull, the herring gull, is frequently found eating garbage at dumps far inland.

See also BIRD.

GULL
A young herring gull pecks at an orange spot on the parent's beak to make it disgorge food.

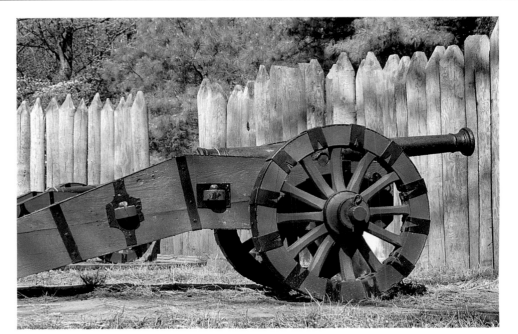

GUN—Cannon

Cannons, such as this one (left) in the fort at Jamestown, Virginia, protected the first colonists in what is now the United States.

GUN—Rifles

The flintlock rifle, called a musket, was loaded with gunpowder down the muzzle. A lead ball was rammed down after it, using the ramrod. The Mauser rifle of 1888 was loaded with cartridge ammunition from a magazine below the breech.

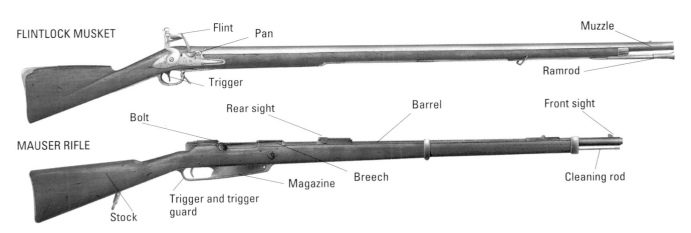

FLINTLOCK MUSKET — Flint — Pan — Muzzle — Trigger — Ramrod

MAUSER RIFLE — Bolt — Rear sight — Barrel — Front sight — Magazine — Breech — Cleaning rod — Trigger and trigger guard — Stock

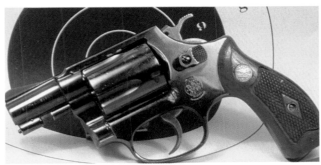

GUN—Revolver

Revolvers, such as the small pistol (left), are guns that store cartridges in a revolving chamber. As each shot is fired, the chamber turns, making another cartridge available.

GUN A gun is a weapon that fires a missile from a tube called a barrel. The missile can be a bullet, a shell, or small pellets. The missile is placed inside the barrel in front of an explosive. The explosive is ignited and gives off large amounts of hot gases. Because they are hot, these gases expand very quickly. This forces the missile down the barrel at a very high speed.

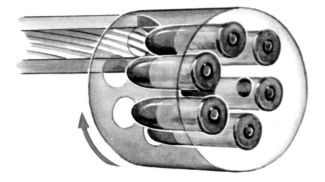

GUN—Rotating chamber

The diagram above illustrates how the chamber of a revolver rotates to bring a bullet into line with the barrel of the gun.

No one knows who invented the gun or even when it was invented. However, evidence suggests that the first guns may have been the cannonlike guns used by the Arabs in North Africa in the 1300s. They consisted of a barrel that was closed at one end. It was mounted on a wooden support. A person called a gunner placed some gunpowder in the open end of the barrel, called the muzzle. He then rammed the gunpowder down into the closed end, called the breech. Then he put a cannonball next to the powder. The gun was fired by placing a lighted wick into a hole in the breech. The wick exploded the gunpowder, and the cannon fired. During the sixteenth century, pistols and other sorts of guns became common. They were all loaded in a similar way. These guns were called muzzle-loaders. They fired a round ball or a number of small pellets.

During the nineteenth century, a different kind of gun was invented. This was the breech-loading gun. These guns were loaded with a cartridge instead of a metal ball. The cartridges were placed near the back of the gun, in the breech. A cartridge has a metal or paper tube containing a bullet, some powder, and a percussion cap. The percussion cap lies at the back of the cartridge. It contains a small amount of explosive. The explosive is very sensitive. It is exploded by striking it with a firing pin. The explosive ignites and sets off the powder charge. By 1900, breech-loading rifles, pistols, and artillery were in general use.

Another invention that was made during the nineteenth century is called rifling. In rifling, a spiral groove is cut on the inside of the barrel. This makes the bullet spin as it leaves the gun. A spinning bullet travels farther and straighter than one that is not spinning.

In 1836, an American inventor, Samuel Colt, patented a revolving pistol. He called it a revolver. It contained a chamber that held five or six cartridges. When the trigger is pulled, the chamber turns around and lines up a cartridge with the barrel. Modern revolvers are very similar to those made by Colt.

Also during the nineteenth century, rifles started to be built with things called magazines. A magazine is a container that holds cartridges. It is placed below the breech. These rifles had a bolt beside the breech. When the bolt was pulled back, the used cartridge was ejected. A new cartridge was fed into the breech by a spring in the magazine. These rifles were used during both world wars and are still used today for hunting.

Today, many guns are automatic or semiautomatic. An example of an automatic gun is the machine gun. Automatic guns keep firing bullets for as long as the trigger is pressed. When a bullet is fired, the explosive in the cartridge gives off hot gases. In an automatic gun, these gases are used to eject the used cartridge. The gases also raise the firing pin. A new cartridge is then fed into the breech and is immediately fired. In a semiautomatic, the used cartridge is ejected in the same way. The breech is loaded automatically, but the trigger has to be pulled for each shot.

GUPPY A guppy is a freshwater fish that belongs to the family Poeciliidae. It is originally from Central and South America but has been introduced by people into waters of the southern United States. Guppies are useful for controlling mosquito larvae in the water and are also popular pet fish. They are often kept in aquariums in homes. Guppies are usually about 1 in. [2.5 cm] long. The males are very colorful. Unlike most fish, the females do not lay eggs but instead give birth to live babies.

See also FISH.

GUPPY
The male guppy (bottom) is often more brightly colored than the female (top), though the female is usually larger.

GYMNOSPERM (jĭm′nə spûrm′) Gymnosperms are plants that bear seeds but have no true flowers or fruit. Their seeds develop in the woody scales of cones in most species. The word *gymnosperm* means "naked seed." Of the six hundred species of gymnosperms, about four hundred are conifers (see CONIFER).

Gymnosperms include such common trees as the pine and spruce and the more exotic ginkgo, yew, and the cycads (see CYCAD; GINKGO). Most gymnosperms are evergreens (see EVERGREEN).

Gymnosperms are known for their high-quality wood. They are also the source of turpentine and other products.

See also ANGIOSPERM; PLANT KINGDOM.

GYPSUM (jĭp′ səm) Gypsum is a very soft, white or yellowish white mineral (see MINERAL). Large beds of gypsum were formed throughout the earth's history by the evaporation of seawater. The United States produces more gypsum than any other country. When gypsum is heated to a low temperature, it loses 75 percent of its water. This process, called calcination, changes it to the white powder called plaster of Paris (see PLASTER OF PARIS). Gypsum in this form is used in the building industry for plasterboard, lath, and wallboard. Gypsum is also used as a filler in paint. The chemical formula of gypsum ($CaSO_4 \cdot 2H_2O$) shows that it is a hydrate of calcium sulfate. A hydrate contains water in addition to its other substances (see HYDRATE).

GYMNOSPERM

Most gymnosperm plants bear cones that contain their seeds. Pictured here are cones of a pine (right), cycad (far right), larch (below), and cedar (below right).

GYROSCOPE (jī'rə skōp´)

A gyroscope is a specially designed wheel. It spins at a very high speed. An object spinning rapidly like this has a very useful property. It tends to stay pointing in the same direction in space. A gyroscope wheel, or rotor, is fixed to an axle. The axle is mounted in a frame, and the frame is suspended inside another frame. The frames are called the gimbals of the gyroscope. They allow the gyroscope to move in any direction as they support it. When the gyroscope is spinning, moving the frame around it does not disturb the gyroscope.

Because a spinning gyroscope always points in the same direction in space, it will seem to tilt during the course of a day. This is because the earth changes position. After twenty-four hours, the axis of the gyroscope will seem to be back in its original position. Actually, however, it is the earth that has moved back to its original position.

A gyroscope wheel is heavy. Most of its weight is in the rim. This gives the wheel a large amount of inertia. It resists attempts to change its position (see INERTIA). If someone tries to tilt the axis, it will move in another direction. It will start to move in a circle. This is known as precession (see PRECESSION).

Gyroscopes are important in navigation. They are used to pilot airplanes and ships. Ordinary magnetic compasses rely on the earth's magnetism to point out directions. The magnetism of the earth, however, varies from place to place. Magnetic compasses cannot always be relied upon, especially near the North and South poles. Gyroscopes can be made to act as compasses. They are not affected by the earth's magnetism. There are several kinds of gyrocompasses (see COMPASS; NAVIGATION).

Ships and submarines have marine gyrocompasses. These have specially weighted frames. The weight acts at right angles to the axis of the gyroscope. The axis of the gyroscope is set to point toward the earth's geographical North Pole. No matter which direction the ship turns, the axis always points to the north. The navigator can set the ship's course accurately by the axis.

Aircraft may have several gyroscopic devices. An important one is the directional gyro. This is rather like a marine gyroscope. It is used for navigation together with a magnetic compass. The other important device is called the artificial horizon. This has a gyroscope that is mounted vertically. It always shows which way is up and which is down, whatever the airplane does. A directional gyro and an artificial horizon are used in the automatic pilot system that many airplanes have.

Gyroscopes are also used to help stop ships from rolling. These gyroscopes are called gyrostabilizers. They usually have one or two very large gyroscopes driven by motors. Smaller gyroscopes control the motors by means of electric switches. The smaller gyroscopes are called control gyros. When the ship starts to roll, the large gyroscopes are switched on. They resist the rolling movement and keep the ship steady.

In most gyroscopes, electric motors keep the rotors spinning. Smaller gyroscopes may be driven by jets of air blowing on the rim of the rotors. *See also* INERTIAL GUIDANCE.

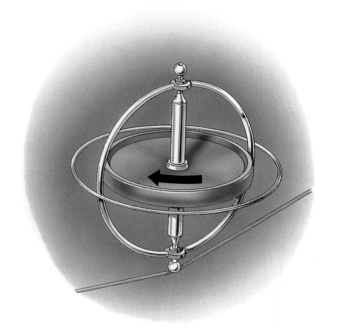

GYROSCOPE

A toy gyroscope will balance on a point and can be made to move along a stretched string like a tightrope walker.